C000172655

THE PLAY OF

THE MONSTER GARDEN

BY DIANE SAMUELS
BASED ON THE NOVEL
BY VIVIEN ALCOCK

HEINEMANN
EDUCATIONAL

Heinemann Educational,
a division of Heinemann Educational Books Ltd,
Halley Court, Jordan Hill, Oxford OX2 8EJ

OXFORD LONDON EDINBURGH
MADRID ATHENS BOLOGNA PARIS
MELBOURNE SYDNEY AUCKLAND SINGAPORE TOKYO
IBADAN NAIROBI HARARE GABORONE PORTSMOUTH NH (USA)

The Play of The Monster Garden was first performed as *Frankie's Monster* at
the Unicorn Theatre for Children on 26 January 1991 and was directed by
Richard Williams.

First published in the *Heinemann Plays* series by Heinemann Educational Ltd
in 1992.

A catalogue record for this book is available from the British Library on
request.

ISBN 435 23284 3

Cover design by Keith Pointing
Designed by Jeffrey White Creative Associates
Typeset by Taurus Graphics, Abingdon, Oxon.
Printed by Clays Ltd, St Ives plc

Contents

Contents

Introduction

What pictures does the word 'Frankenstein' conjure up for you?
A mad scientist digging around in graveyards for pieces of
bodies which he can sew together to make a creature of his
own? A wild thunderstorm bringing to violent life an enormous
man with bolts through his neck and huge boots on his feet?
People running away and screaming as the 'monster' walks
towards them, his arms held out in front ready for the kill?
Whatever it brings to mind, you can be sure that the story of
Frankenstein and his monster has a feeling of horror about it.
Fear and danger are the main ingredients.

It is surprising to discover that the story of 'Frankenstein' was
first written about 180 years ago by a nineteen-year-old woman
called Mary Shelley. She wrote it after an evening of ghost story
tellings with her husband, the poet John Shelley, and their
friend, also a poet, Lord Bryon. After frightening each other
with tales of dead spirits haunting the living, they decide to set
a challenge to see who could write the best new ghost story. No
one knows what became of the stories written by Bryon and
Shelley, but Mary's has become one of the most well-known
horror yarns of all times.

Vivien Alcock also writes ghost stories and she started her
book, *The Monster Garden*, with the intention of writing 'a
modern story based on the tale of Frankenstein which took into
account modern scientific developments'. She also wondered
'how the monster might develop if it was created and reared by
children'. The result is a funny, touching, thought-provoking
account of how the daughter of a 'high-up scientist' makes her
own monster and then has to deal with the living consequences
of what she has done. Will she get caught? Will the monster be

experimented on if it is found? Who should she get to help her? Who are her real friends? How can she deal with so much responsibility? This is a story about a monster in which horror is, surprisingly, in very short supply even though there is plenty of excitement. But then, as the narrator in the play says 'Monsters are never what they seem.'

In a book, it is easy to describe a monster and leave the rest to reader's imagination. In a play, the big question is, how do you actually make it work on the stage? I wanted to give you, the performers, the chance to be creative and decide exactly how to do this for yourselves. I have provided lines in the play for the narrator who describes what Monnie does, feels or looks like to give you some help and I hope that you will have a great deal of fun working out how to bring your own Monnie to theatrical life. In the Unicorn Theatre production of the play, the narrators took the form of two dolphins and Monnie herself was represented by a spotlight which bounced around the stage whilst a cello played her voice. In the Copthall School version, sinister ringmaster characters sat around the audience and delivered the narrators whilst Monnie was playing by a number of dancers, more and more of whom came on to the stage as Monnie got bigger and bigger. Monnie can be played in any number of ways; it is up to you to find the one that suits you.

After the play text, you will find ideas for follow-up work. The first section, *Keeping Track,* can be followed scene-by-scene as you read the play and contains questions and simple exercises to help you think more clearly and deeply about what is raised in each scene. The second section, *Explorations*, has larger activities and encourages you to think more broadly about the themes and issues raised by the play as a whole. It also contains some exercises which will help if you are putting on a performance of the play.

Diane Samuels

List of Scenes

Act One

Act Two

Act One

Narrator She shouldn't have done it.
She didn't mean to, but that's no excuse.
She should have known better with a name like
hers.

Scene One: *The Creek*

The sound of waves and gulls.

*A wash of blue light to create the effect of a small,
pebble-covered beach sheltered by a cliff and
rocks.*

*Frankie, an eleven-year-old girl, and her eleven-
year-old friend, Heather, are half-dressed, half-
drying themselves with towels after swimming in
the sea.*

*Hazel is looking out to sea. She is watching
something.*

Hazel Can you see it?

Frankie What?

Hazel Moving out there … Look! It did it again!

Frankie What did what?

Hazel Leaped out of the water. You must be able to see
it.

Frankie All I can see is the sea and the sky and some
poxy seagulls.

Hazel I bet it's the dolphin.

Frankie It can't be. No one's seen it for ages.

Hazel What else would jump on the surface like that?

Frankie The light's just playing tricks on the waves and
your eyes are being taken in.

Hazel Why don't you want it to be the dolphin?

Frankie You can't make it up if it isn't there!

Hazel Just 'cause you can't see it, doesn't mean that it isn't there!

Frankie	Just 'coz you think you can see it, doesn't mean that it is!
Hazel	Just 'cause your father wouldn't take you to his laboratory today, doesn't mean that you have to take it out on me!
Frankie	I'm not taking anything out on anyone!
Hazel	Yes you are! You've been grumping since we met up.
Frankie	I've not been. I'm having a very nice time!
Hazel	You should have just told him that you wanted to go too.
Frankie	Why should I go into a stuffy lab when I can come out into the sunshine and go swimming in my favourite creek! It's much better here.
Hazel	Usually, it is. Usually it's the best place to be. Usually, it cheers us up.

Frankie speaks aggressively

Frankie	I am cheered up!
Hazel	Then why are you shouting at me!
Frankie	This is what I do when I'm happy.
Hazel	Well, it's not making me very happy!

Hazel storms off to another part of the beach to put on her shoes and socks.

Both girls put on their final pieces of clothing in silence and at a distance from each other.

Frankie finishes dressing first. Hazel is looking for something in her bag.

Frankie thinks then moves towards Hazel.

Frankie	Hazel?
Hazel	Have you seen my comb?

Frankie looks around.

Frankie	No. But …
Hazel	I can't find it. It's not here.

Frankie	Maybe you didn't pack it.
Hazel	I know I did.
Frankie	You usually do forget something.
Hazel	I definitely put it in.
Frankie	Why don't you borrow my brush?
Hazel	You know it's not right for my hair.
Frankie	It'd be better than nothing.

Frankie goes to her bag and gets out her brush.
She holds it out to Hazel.
Hazel looks, thinks, then takes the brush.

Frankie	I'm sorry, Haze.
Hazel	I just wish you'd get moody with someone else.

She tries to use the brush not very successfully.

Hazel	We should invent a hair comb and brush which we could both use.
Frankie	Or we should be able to change our hair when we want.
Hazel	Like those dolls with a key in their back and when you turn it their hair grows.
Frankie	Only theirs just gets longer or shorter.
Hazel	But ours would get curlier or thinner …
Frankie	Or turn different colours.
Hazel	Anything we wanted.
Frankie	Without having to go to the hairdresser.
Hazel	Just by thinking about it.
Frankie	Like having magic powers.
Hazel	Or it would be done by science, by eating something.
Frankie	You'd probably have to have an injection if it was done by science.
Hazel	I don't mind injections.
Frankie	I always get a lump or a rash on my arm.

Hazel	This one wouldn't do that. Your dad could invent it.
Frankie	For all I know he probably has already. And David will know all about it too when he gets home. I'll be the only one who doesn't.
Hazel	But David's much more interested in that stuff than you are.
Frankie	That's what Dad said.
Hazel	He probably thought that you'd get bored.
Frankie	That's what David said. Spotty oaf!

Frankie mimics David:

'Face it, Frankie, you wouldn't understand a thing. You'd just fidget and be a real pain.'

Hazel	He was right about the last thing.
Frankie	He's not right about anything. Especially not about me!
Hazel	You can be a real pain.
Frankie	Only when things aren't fair!
Hazel	You sound just like Julia Hobson. 'S'not fair! S'not fair!'
Frankie	I'm going to get you for that, Hazel Brent!
Hazel	No chance, Frances Stein!

Hazel darts away and runs across to Frankie's clothes.

She grabs a packet of sweets out of her jacket and waves it at her tauntingly.

Frankie	Give them back!
Hazel	You don't deserve them!

Frankie chases Hazel who keeps just getting away.

Frankie	I paid for those!
Hazel	I'll give you the money tomorrow!
Frankie	You haven't got it!
Hazel	Your teeth'll fall out!
Frankie	Yours already have!

Hazel   At least they're not rotten like yours.

Frankie   Or maggoty like your breath!

Hazel   Or stale like your sandwiches!

Frankie   Or smelly like your feet!

Hazel   Or crooked like your nose!

Frankie   Or flat like your jokes!

Hazel   Or scummy like your bath water!

Frankie takes a leap and lands on Hazel, pulling her to the ground.

Frankie   Porcupine!

Hazel   Frankenstein!

Hazel struggles to be free.

Hazel   Frankenstein!

Frankie struggles to get the sweets.

Frankie   What did you say!

Hazel   Frankenstein! Frankenstein! Frankenstein!

Frankie   You sound just like those stupid kids at school! Can't you think of anything better!

Hazel   Watch out! Igor's coming to get you!

Frankie   Heard it before! Just give me back my sweets!

Frankie tries to prize open Hazel's hand.

Frankie   Youve got hands like claws!

Hazel   All the better for keeping hold!

They struggle some more.

Frankie gets half the packet and the sweets tumble out.

They collapse on the beach, side by side, catching their breath.

Frankie looks at the packet in her hand.

Frankie   I got those for sharing. We could have had half each.

Hazel   Sweets are for fighting over.

Frankie	Close your eyes.
Hazel	Why?
Frankie	Guess the flavour.
Hazel	Promise it isn't a trick.
Frankie	Promise.

Hazel closes her eyes and Frankie puts a sweet in her mouth.

She sucks and thinks.

Hazel	Green?
Frankie	Right! How did you know?
Hazel	Natural brilliance! Your turn.

Frankie closes her eyes and Hazel puts in a sweet.

She sucks and thinks.

Frankie	Is it green again?
Hazel	No. Yellow.
Frankie	It doesn't taste yellow at all.
Hazel	The real test would be to do it with Smarties.
Frankie	No one could do that. They all taste the same.
Hazel	Except the orange ones.
Frankie	That's not much help.

Hazel gets up.

Hazel	Nothing is impossible.
Frankie	You always say that.
Hazel	Only to cheer you up.
Frankie	It doesn't change things just because you say it.
Hazel	I'm sure he will take you to the lab. One day he will.
Frankie	That'll be the day after you see your dolphin.

Scene Two: *The Stein home downstairs into David's bedroom*

Five characters gather as if round a table eating a family meal. They include Professor Stein, Frankie's father, a preoccupied and busy scientist in his fifties; David, Frankie's brother, who is fifteen and Frankie herself. The other two characters are representations of Frankie's mother and elder brother Ben.

Narrator The family Stein …
Five characters, including Prof. Stein, Frankie and David, gather as if round a table eating a family meal.

Once totalled five.
All sitting round the table.
Then Mrs Stein died.

One gets up and goes.

Leaving four round the table.
Then Ben went off to college.

Another gets up and goes.

Leaving three round the table:
Half as many as there'd been at first,
the Professor and his two youngest.

Frankie, David and Prof. Stein are eating their meal.

The atmosphere is very restrained.

David I thought I might write up a report on the visit to the laboratory today, Father.

Frankie What? Spend your time writing a report during the summer holidays! You're mad.

Prof. Stein replies in a way that suggests he is preoccupied by other things:

Prof. Stein Certainly. If it would be of use to you, David. Excellent idea.

Frankie What did you do there?

David It's above your head, Frankie. Your brain

	couldn't take it.
Frankie	What do you mean?

David ignores Frankie and talks to Prof. Stein:

David	Father, shall I give it to you to read when it's done?
Prof. Stein	I might not be able to look at it for a few weeks.
David	I'd appreciate your comments.

Prof. Stein replies in a preoccupied way:

Prof. Stein	I'll see what I can do.

Frankie addresses David again:

Frankie	Can I see it when you've done it?
David	I don't think so, Frankie. You wouldn't be able to understand it.
Frankie	I would.
David	Didn't I ever tell you that females have got smaller brains than males?
Frankie	What's size got to do with it! Elephants have got enormous brains and they probably still think the world's flat.

Prof. Stein shows signs of irritation.

Prof. Stein	Hmph.
David	May I be excused, please?
Prof. Stein	Hasn't Mrs Drake left us some ice cream for pudding?
David	In the kitchen.
Prof. Stein	Maybe Frances would like to go and see what flavour it is.
Frankie	It's strawberry.
Prof. Stein	I'm not sure I want any of that.
David	I don't think I could eat any more. I'm full up.
Prof. Stein	Perhaps we'll leave the strawberry ice cream for when Frances has some of her friends round.
Frankie	I want some now.
David	Can I go upstairs then?

Prof. Stein I suggest that both of you do whatever you want to. But not too much noise.

Prof. Stein talks to himself.

Prof. Stein Now, where on earth did I put that file?

Prof. Stein exits.

David hastily gets up.

David Looks like you're having the ice cream on your own.

Frankie Looks like you're up to something.

David Just keep your nose to yourself.

He makes to exit.

Frankie Aren't you going to help me clear up?

David Have you got something better to do?

Frankie Yes.

David Too bad.

David exits. He is walking slightly stiffly as if trying not to spill something in his pocket.

Frankie watches him.

David walks to his bedroom

Company follow David in his tracks, guessing his motives.

Narrator Maybe he did it to escape the shadow
Of his student brother,
To be like his father
The high up professor?

P'raps he just likes to experiment
With anything he can,
From frogs and worms,
To leaves and stems,
And this was something new?

Maybe he wants to know
How living thinks work,
Needs to play with cell upon cell,
Building them up like pieces of Lego,
Digging down to their very heart,

To discover the secret of life?

By now, David has removed a test tube from his pocket and is busy using a glass tube to transfer the substance in the dish to a petrie dish coated with red jelly.

Frankie is now standing at bedroom door almost falling over trying to see what he is up to.

Frankie What's that you've nicked?

David turns with a start.

David What the hell are you doing here you little squirt? I told you never to come into my room.

Frankie I'm not in your room. I'm looking into it from the doorway. You'll never be a scientist until you learn to get things right.

David Just close the door and go away!

Frankie nips closer to him.

Frankie Let me see it.

David Get out of my room!

Frankie Only if you tell me what it is!

David You wouldn't understand.

Frankie Stealing from a laboratory is a crime.

David You don't know what you're talking about.

Frankie A serious crime.

David What makes you think I've stolen anything.

Frankie Ever since you got home with Dad you've been acting cagey. And where else would you have got it?

David None of your business!

Frankie That stuff might be dangerous.

David Oh, you're the expert are you!

Frankie It might burn you down to the bone if you get it on you.

David It's not that sort of thing.

Frankie What sort of thing is it then?

David	Frankie, you're better off leaving things alone if you don't understand them.
Frankie	I don't see you leaving anything alone and I bet you don't understand either.
David	I know a lot more than you.
Frankie	Then tell me. I won't tell Dad.
	Pause. David sizes up the situation.
David	Do the words 'Genetic Engineering' mean anything to you?
Frankie	We haven't got to that at school yet.
David	Well, it's very exciting, very important. A way of creating new forms of life.
Frankie	Monsters!
David	Not monsters! Organisms that behave in a way nothing has behaved in before.
Frankie	That *is* monsters!
David	You're so ignorant.
Frankie	There could be anything living in that.
David	Not living in it exactly. This is more like the seeds of something.
Frankie	Of what?
David	I'm not a hundred per cent sure.
Frankie	But you're going to grow it and find out.
David	Might do.
Frankie	I want some.
David	Oh come on, Frankie, this isn't a packet of crisps. It's living cells.
Frankie	*Stolen* living cells.
David	If you go now, I'll give you 50p.
Frankie	Half of it.
David	A pound.
Frankie	You don't need it all.
David	What do you think you'll do with it? You haven't got an incubator or a microscope

or anything, not even brains. It'd just be a
waste. It'd be throwing the stuff away.

Frankie Either you give me some or I tell Dad.

David You said you wouldn't!

Frankie Well, you shouldn't have taken it if you didn't
want problems.

David It was only left overs.

Frankie You didn't ask if you could have it, though, did
you?

David I would have done if I'd had the chance.

Frankie Liar.

Pause.

David I want to discover something of my own.

Frankie So do I.

David I want to show them what I can do. Show them
without anyone poking their nose in.

Frankie All right. Not half. Just a little bit, David, a very
little bit.

David And if I do, you'll go away?

Frankie Immediately.

David And not sneak into my room again?

Frankie I didn't sneak!

David Well?

Frankie All right.

David And not tell a soul, not a single soul.

Frankie No one.

David Not even that friend of yours.

Frankie Her name's Hazel.

David Especially not her. She can't keep anything to
herself.

Frankie   Don't be rude about my friends.

David Just agree to the conditions, Frankie.

Frankie OK!

David   Here you are then.

He takes a glass stick and carefully catches some of the substance on to it.

Frankie peers at the tube.

Frankie   Are you sure it's not just frogspawn?

David   Don't be silly.

He holds out the glass stick towards her.

Frankie   Can't I have some of that red stuff to grow it on?

David   It's called blood agar. Get your terms right.

Frankie   Give me some then.

David   I don't have any to spare.

Frankie   Yes you do.

David   That wasn't part of our bargain. You just said some of this. Do you want it or not?

Frankie   What'll I put it in.

David   Your hand.

Frankie puts her hands behind her back as though afraid to hold it.

Frankie   I can't.

David   It won't bite, stupid.

Frankie   How do you know!

David   It's microscopic.

Frankie   Well ... I might damage it.

David   All right, take a slide from there.

Frankie takes a slide.

David   Here,

He drops the jelly on to the slide.

Now beat it.

Frankie   What'll I grow it on?

David   You're the scientist. You work it out.

Frankie hesitantly starts to retreat.

And bring that slide back when you've finished.

They cost money.

Frankie exits.

Narrator   Maybe she did it because she was
Fed up of being the youngest girl
In a family of boys,
The one they forgot to notice?
Maybe she shouldn't have done it at all.
She should have known better with
A name like hers.

Frankie's bedroom space is created.

A bed, window frame and pot of African violets.

Frankie looks at the slide inquisitively.

Frankie   This is no good. It'll dry up.

She takes the dirty saucer from under the African violets.

It'll have to rough it. No petrie dish, no choice.

Now she has the slide in one hand and the saucer in the other.

She half-heartedly makes to tip the jelly into the saucer.

Sorry about the dirt. You'll just have to adapt.

She stops herself.

No! I need some water or something. Food. Only one thing for it.

She puts down the slide and saucer, then takes off a badge she is wearing and jabs her finger with the pin.

Ouch!

She squeezes her cut finger over the saucer.

No agar but enough blood.
This should do.

She carefully tips the jelly into the blood-stained saucer and looks hard.

I hope he's right about it being alive.
You're not doing much are you? How would I

know if you were dead? You'd probably look just the same. The thing is that I need you to keep on living, maybe even grow a little, just a bit, to show that this is working. Then they'll say: 'Fine stuff, Frances, you've broken new ground.' or 'Remarkable achievement for one so young and so female.' And I'll have helped push back the barriers of Knowledge, and David will think, 'Frankie, she's an expert in these matters, I'll ask her.' Then he'll want to do experiments with me. Dad too. He'll ask me to read what he's written for his journals and sit after dinner drawing diagrams to help me understand his latest ideas. So, you see, there's a lot depending on this. It's important. And I'm sorry about the chipped saucer and no proper equipment, but penicillin was discovered because something dripped where it shouldn't have, so we shouldn't be put off. There's still a very good chance of success. Got that? A very good chance!

Frankie puts the saucer by the window.

Scene Three: *Frankie's Bedroom*

Frankie is in bed.

Thunder, rain and lightning effects created by the Company on stage.

As the Narrator speaks, the sound of quiet, but gradually increasing rumblings of a storm can be heard in the background.

Narrator   Sometimes, somewhere, a parcel of air
begins to get hot.
Like a balloon it starts to rise
Through the cold air around it.
Up it goes, higher and higher,
Faster, and faster,
Letting out heat, building up pressure,
Electric charge in the dark, dark clouds.
Then when the cloud can hold no more,

A huge, hot spark breaks free!

There is a flash of lightning and the sound of falling rain.

Count the seconds after the flash.
One and two and three ...

There is a crash of thunder.

Five seconds makes a mile.
Under a mile away.

There is another flash of lightning.

One and ...

Another crash of thunder.

Overhead!

Frankie sits up, suddenly awake. She is exhilerated by the storm.

Another flash of lightning followed by thunder.

Frankie   What a whoppa! I wouldn't fly a kite in it!

Another flash, another thunder clap.

Frankie   Sour milk for breakfast!

Another flash, as if coming in through the window, and clap.

Frankie winces and guards her eyes from the brightness.

Leave my eyes alone!

She turns away from the window and goes back to sleep.

Company create chaos of storm.

Narrator   No reason, no rhyme!

Can't control a storm!
Electric chaos
Fills the sky.

Can't catch a flash!
Stripes of power
Dart and dive.

Can't trap particles
Out and free to

clash and bash each other and
Anything else that gets in the way!

A flash of lightning hits the saucer.

A light shines from the saucer.

Something changing, something alive.
Stillness is shattered.
The cells divide:
One cell to two cells.
Two cells to four cells.
Multiplying life.
Own course set.
Growth unleashed.
Creation begins.
And things,
Oh things
Will never be quite the same again.

Heartbeat pulsing in the darkness.

*Light of dawn and birds singing fade in over
heartbeat.*

*The saucer is soot-blackened and cracked.
African violet is knocked over, and has fallen
messily on to the floor.*

Frankie wakes up.

Frankie   Lie in till late today.

She stretches.

Mmmm.

*A company member zaps on, jangles the broken
pottery, then zaps off.*

Frankie   What?

Frankie sits up in bed.

What a mess! Oh no, all over the floor.

She gets out of bed.

Should have closed the window.

She starts to pick up the plant.

Poor plant.

Company member zaps across the stage to beside or under the bed.

Frankie is terrified.

Frankie Aaaaaaah! What is it!

Heartbeat loud and fast.

Narrator Quivering, quivering
Shivering grey,
Lump of goo
With see-through skin
And bright red slits
Where eyes might be.

Frankie Frankie, calm down. It's probably only a mouse. Just catch it and take it out to the garden.

Hearbeat loud and fast.

Frankie kneels down and looks under the bed.

Frankie Now where are ...

She leaps back.

Aaaagh! It's got red eyes! Bright red eyes! It's not a mouse. It's my experiment.

Company member whizzes away from Frankie and hovers near a piece of the plant.

Frankie Ugh! A mouse-sized lump of living snot.

Company make popping and slurpy sucking noises of monster searching hungrily for food.

Company create effect of violet being explored and tasted.

Narrator Pop goes the skin,
Out comes a tentacle
Feeling the floor
Spreading its slithering,
Squirming jelly in search
Of food.

Frankie Oh no! My African violet! Don't eat it! You horrible see-through blob, leave my plant alone!

Monster rejects violet. More slurping, popping and searching for food.

Frankie   I've got to get rid of it! One stamp with my foot
and it'll be dead! Right!

*She goes to stamp, holds her foot above a
squirming, slurping member of the chorus.*

Frankie agonises with herself:

Frankie   Go on Frankie, do it!

She takes her foot away and backs off.

Frankie   I can't squash you. I'm no good at killing things.
Not even flies. Not even you. It'd be much
better if you'd just go away and die. Please,
please, die. I mean you shouldn't have come to
life in the first place. Dying would be the right
thing. It really would.

*Urgent slurping sound and stretching out for more
food. It is very hungry.*

Frankie   I said don't look at me like that. I haven't got
any food. You'll have to starve. Just go away. Go
away!

More hungry noises.

Frankie   I haven't got anything to give you!

Narrator   Hunger is hard to hear.
How piercing a baby's cry
How sharp a kitten's starving call
How stabbing a puppy's plea.
An empty belly can't be left
To rumble and groan and hurt.
Quell the cry.
Feed the soul.
All it takes is a finger prick.

Scene Four: *The Stein home downstairs into
Frankie's bedroom*

Prof. Stein and David are sitting eating breakfast.

David is reading a large book on biochemistry.

*Prof. Stein is concentrating on his newspaper but
displays a half-interest in David:*

Prof. Stein	Are you going out this morning David?
David	No. I'll be working on something in my room.
Prof. Stein	Really? Mrs Drake seemed to think that you'd be going into town.
David	No, that's Frankie.
Prof. Stein	What is Frankie?
David	Who's meant to be going into town this morning.
Prof. Stein	But not you?
David	No, not me.
Prof. Stein	I lose track. I really do.
David	Can't think why she's late for breakfast.

Prof. Stein is now totally preoccupied with the newspaper.

Prof. Stein	No. Neither can I.

Pause.

Frankie enters looking shocked.

She sits down and takes a little breakfast. She doesn't eat very much.

They eat in silence.

Frankie looks at the finger she pricked last night, shakes and sucks it.

David	If you've got a splinter, you should get it out with a needle.
Frankie	I just cut it.
David	It shouldn't hurt that much.
Frankie	I cut it twice.
David	How come?
Prof. Stein	Frances, tell Mrs Drake that I will not be having supper at home today.
Frankie	Yes, father.

Pause as Prof. Stein folds up his paper and rises.

Is Ben still coming back next week?

Prof. Stein   Mrs Drake has all the details. Ask her.

He starts to go.

There are some letters on the table in the hall that David said you'd post for me.

Frankie shoots David a dirty look.

Goodbye, both of you.

Prof. Stein exits.

Frankie   Thanks David.

David   Well, you're going out this morning.

Frankie   He asked you first.

David   Didn't feel like it.

Frankie   Well, neither do I.

David   Oooooh. Touchy, touchy.

Frankie   It's just that …

She's about to tell him something but is uncertain.

Well, you see …

David   What?

She changes her tack:

Frankie   How is your you-know-what getting on?

David   My which?

Frankie   Your what's it … your 'frogspawn'?

David   None of your business. How's yours?

Frankie   Different.

David   How?

Frankie   It's quite big now.

David replies disbelievingly:

David   Is it?

Frankie   I haven't quite worked out what to feed it on. They seem to eat quite a lot, don't they?

David   Not really.

Frankie   And grow very quickly.

David   Not especially.

Frankie   Has yours grown much?

David   Don't be so stupid. In one night? Of course it hasn't. You've got no idea have you?

Frankie   I was just thinking what I should do with it if it did grow. Grow into something disgusting.

David   'Disgusting' isn't a scientific word, Frankie.

Frankie   I mean, something really horrible. Revolting. Tentacles and arms and slits in its side …

David   Bet you anything it won't do that.

Frankie   But what if it did?

David   It won't!

Frankie   You can't be sure!

David   Yes I can.

Frankie   You can't.

David   I can because it's dead. D E A D Dead! Wasn't worth taking in the first place.

He takes a package out of his pocket and spills the contents into his hand.

Crumbled up. Like an old rubber.

Frankie   Is that the other half?

David   Yours will go like this too.

Frankie   What have you done to it?

David   Cut up sections for my slides.

Frankie   How?

David   With a razor blade. It's useless not having the right equipment …

Frankie   How could you do that? You could have hurt it.

David   All biologists have to cut things up. It's part of the job. You're too squeamish, that's your trouble.

Frankie   It might have been alive.

David   If it was, it was only cells. When it comes to proper research, you can't be put off by what something looks like or whether or not it has

'feelings'. You've got to find out all about it,
learning what it's made of. You've got to try out
everything so that you know all there is to
know. Experiment on it in every way.

Frankie   Every way?

David   Yes. That's what you made it for in the first
place isn't it?

Frankie   But what if ...

David   Don't forget to post those letters.

David exits.

Frankie is stuck to the spot.

Frankie   What if you just want it to stop? Creepy, slimy
snot-ball. I wish it'd die.

Frankie moves as if going up to her room.

Narrator   Wishing is what people do
When they feel they've lost control.
Cross your fingers,
Touch wood,
Hope your hardest,
Pray a prayer,
And all may change for the best
When the worst has taken hold.
Wishing is simpler than doing
Like saying, 'Not me! I can't!'

Frankie   Not cut it up. Not hurt it.
Just so as it wasn't there. Didn't exist.
Wasn't in my room, sliding all over the floor.

Frankie listens as if by her bedroom door.

Nothing.

She listens again.

Nor afraid to go into your own room are you?

She pauses and listens.

Yes.

Pause.

Some scientist! Go on.

She enters.

Narrator   Can wishes come true? Can they?

Scene Five: *Frankie's bedroom*

Company members create shape of cocooned monster, deathly still in the middle of the room.

Frankie   Someone's left a parcel on the floor. A cling-film parcel with food in it?

Frankie creeps up and looks at the shape.

No. It's not a parcel. It's the thing. It is. Like it's all been wrapped up. So still. Still as death.

She suddenly realises what's happened.

It's died. Like I wanted. It has. It has.

She is relieved.

All for the best. Like at great aunt Joan's funeral. That's a point. Bury it in the garden next to the goldfish graves. Yes. That's what I'll do. Get it buried straight away. Then I'll still have time to go out and meet Hazel.
Better find something to pick it up with and wrap it in.

Frankie turns her back on the 'parcel', searches for and pulls out lots of wrapping paper and bags from a drawer.

Frankie   Hurrah, hurrah. Monster rest in peace.

Narrator   Far more than sleep,
Far less than death,
A comfortable coma.
Suspended on a breath,
Like a pea in a pod,
A caterpillar in a cocoon.
A snake in its last skin.

The heartbeat begins pulsating quietly.

Things are changing again.

Frankie sorts through the bags and paper.

Frankie   I'll need to wrap it up in a few layers or it might infect the soil or something, and then the flowers will start growing funny.

The cocoon begins to move with a pulsating movement in time with the increasingly loud heartbeat.

Frankie   Got the bags. Just need sellotape to make a parcel …

Frankie gropes in the drawer.

Deep moan and loud pulsating of heartbeat.

Monster breaks out of cocoon and moves up to right behind Frankie.

Frankie turns round still searching for the sellotape.

Frankie   Aaaahhh!

Monster screeches and jumps back.

Frankie is shocked.

Frankie   You died! I saw you! Why aren't you dead any more?

Monster jumps back.

Frankie   What's happened to you? Why are you bigger? Why are you different?

Monster jumps back again and makes a burping sound.

Frankie   I get it – that stuff around you was a cocoon wasn't it? Why hasn't it made you beautiful?

Monster jumps back twice and burps each time.

Frankie is half-laughing and half-crying.

Frankie   You're so revolting! Like a baby pig with bits of flaky octopus hanging off you.

Monster jumps forward twice and burps simultaneously.

Frankie laughs manically.

Frankie   Stop it!

Monster jumps forward once and backward once, burping simultaneously.

Frankie laughs hysterically.

Frankie   Stay still! Stay still!

Monster bounces and burps around the room.

Frankie laughs uncontrollably.

Scene Six: *Frankie's bedroom*

Frankie is standing in the middle of the room holding a large box.

The monster is looking at her expectantly.

Frankie talks to monster as she unpacks the box.

Frankie   Here's some food.
Milk ... bread ... boiled eggs ... carrots ... a lemon ... raw eggs just in case boiled are no good ... spinach ... chocolate ... cornflakes ... tin of beans ... some tea bags ... Should find something you like.
Better had. I need my blood. Just hope human food doesn't poison you, or make you grow very big, or be sick ... all over my bedroom. And I'll have to pretend I've got a bad stomach and it was me ...

Monster watches at a distance.

Frankie   Go on. Eat it. It's for you.

Monster oozes over to the food and explores it.

Frankie   I can't look after you all the time. Not on my own. I need help. I'll have to tell someone.
Hazel. Better phone her.

Makes a move. Thinks. Stops.

Monster starts to eat hungrily.

Frankie   No, just being my friend isn't good enough for something like this. It must be someone who knows a lot. More than me and Hazel anyway.

Monster continues to eat at a fast rate and

Frankie turns her attention to it:

Frankie   How can you eat so quickly, Gammy-Red-Eyes!

She continues to consider who to tell:

Also, this person has to be able to keep secrets.
And Hazel's terrible at keeping secrets. Worse
than me. Someone without lots of friends to tell
…

*Monster finishes and Frankie turns her attention
to it again:*

Frankie   Finished already! That's disgusting!

She returns to her own thoughts:

I know! Julia Hobson. She's the cleverest in the
class.
What do you think, monster? Julia Hobson?

Monster burps.

Scene Seven: *Frankie's bedroom*

Narrator   Monsters are never what you expect.
They can tear down buildings, hold people
in the palm of their hand;
Burn the air with their smouldering breath,
Ooze with mud and pus and slime.
And sometimes, just sometimes, they can
be nothing like this at all.

A scream is heard.

*Lights up on Julia and Frankie. Julia is a school
friend of Frankie's, also eleven years old.*

*Julia is standing on the bed and Frankie is on the
floor.*

Monster is cowering in the corner.

*Julia is in a state of shock. She is keen to keep as
far away from monster as possible.*

*She is also holding her finger away from her in
mid-air.*

Julia   It felt horrible!

Frankie   I've not touched it yet.

Julia   And those eyes!

Frankie   I know, they are very red. But you get used to them.

Julia   It's like a lump of jelly. All the wrong shape. No hair, no nose, no ears, no feet, no hands ...

Something stirs under the bed.

Julia   Where is it!

Frankie   Still under the bed ... somewhere. I think it's afraid of getting poked again.

Julia   It'll do something to us. We've got to get out of here!

Frankie   You can go if you want. Only remember you promised not to tell.

Julia   I can't leave you with that.

Frankie   I've managed to survive so far.

Uneasy pause as Julia wipes her finger on her clothes.

Frankie looks at Julia's finger.

Frankie   Would you like some sandpaper or can I cut it off for you?

Julia examines her finger.

Julia   It feels funny.

Frankie is ashamed.

Frankie   Sorry. Does it?

Julia   Do you know ... is that thing poisonous?

Frankie is uncertain.

Frankie   I don't think so ... Well ... Don't know really. I mean ... you might be right. There's some Dettol in the bathroom if you ...

Monster slowly emerges from the corner.

Music.

Julia sees it immediately.

Julia	Aaaaah! There it is! There it is!
	Frankie pretends to be calm.
Frankie	It won't hurt you.
	Heartbeat pulsing faster.
	It's very shy.
Julia	It's waiting to pounce.
	Frankie holds out her hand and inches nearer to monster.
Frankie	It's just a baby.
Julia	Be careful!
	Frankie speaks gently to Monster.
Frankie	You don't need to be afraid.
	Pause. Music.
	Waiting for what will happen.
	Monster leaps with a flurry of high-pitched sound to lie on Frankie's lap.
	Frankie is very taken aback and uncertain.
	Frankie tries to be convincing.
Frankie	See. It's OK really.
Julia	You're mad, Frankie.
	Frankie tentatively strokes monster.
Frankie	It's not very slimy at all.
	A more melodious sound. The monster stops quivering.
Julia	I feel sick.
Frankie	I did at first too. Now, I know it a bit better.
	Pauses to look at Monster as she strokes.
	Doesn't it look like an overgrown jelly baby?
Julia	I just think that the way it is and everything is a terrible mistake.
Frankie	That's because you've never seen anything like it before.
	She looks at it again.

These stumpy bits ... it walks on these.
They must be its legs.

The monster makes a sharp movement.

It smiled at me!

Julia How d'you mean?

Frankie See that slit, there ... it made a sort of U shape ...

The monster moves sharply again.

Frankie See!

Julia How do you know that's a smile?

Frankie It felt like one.

Julia It didn't feel like one to me. Put it down, Frankie, it might give you a disease ... there's something faulty about it.

Frankie It's not faulty. It's different.

Julia You did ask me here for my advice.

Frankie And your help.

Julia I just think you're being very silly.
You don't know what they do in the laboratories. You've not been there, have you?

Frankie Dad wouldn't take me.

Julia Exactly. None of us knows. They could be making secret weapons ...

Frankie laughs.

Frankie Oh, come on, you don't believe that do you?

Monster moves intricately and makes a sort of mimic laughing sound.

Frankie Look, Julia, look at it's mouth now ... it's a figure eight! Amazing!

Julia They might be making secret weapons.
Haven't you ever heard of germ warfare?

Frankie My monster's too big to be a germ.

Julia But it could be anything. You've got to tell your father.

Frankie I can't.

Julia	You'll have to give it back.
Frankie	No!
Julia	You'll have to Frankie. You can't keep a thing like this hidden for ever.
Frankie	I promised David I wouldn't tell Dad. I always keep my promises.
	Pause.
Julia	All right then, you don't have to tell your father. You can take it to the lab yourself and say you found it outside.
Frankie	I don't trust them.
Julia	But they know what they're doing.
Frankie	That doesn't mean they won't do anything horrid to it.
Julia	They might have hundreds of these ... creatures up there already. They might know exactly how to look after it.
Frankie	Like cutting it up and putting it in test tubes.
Julia	But maybe that's the best thing for it. Maybe they're inventing a cure for cancer or something.
Frankie	I thought you said they made secret weapons.
Julia	I don't know, do I. I'm just trying to help. That's why you asked me here.
	Monster starts to form a new shape.
	A throbbing sound is heard.
Frankie	I'm sorry. It's just that if it got hurt I'd ...
Julia	Frankie, it's looking at you in a funny way.
	Frankie shows her hands to Monster.
Frankie	Yes, these are my hands Hands.
	Responsive sound, as if working 'hands' out.
	Julia watches monster.
Julia	It's not a proper animal, is it? It's just something

	made up in a lab, like nylon or plastic. It hasn't got a soul.
Frankie	Yes, it has. It's alive isn't it!
Julia	But it was made by people, not born in a natural way.
Frankie	The lightning brought it to life. Lightning's natural. Anyway, what does it matter how it got here? It's what it's like now that counts.
Julia	So what are you going to do about it? It's getting bigger all the time.
Frankie	What about finding somewhere else to put it, somewhere with more space, somewhere secret?
Julia	Then what?
Frankie	If you think I should tell an older person, I was thinking of telling Ben.
Julia	Who's he?
Frankie	My biggest brother. He's on holiday in France. He'll be back next week.
Julia	Will he know what to do?
Frankie	Oh yes. He's a scientist – well, a student really, of chemistry, but he'll think of a way of saving it.

Monster starts to grow slightly and gradually change shape again unnoticed by the girls.

Intermittent noises of growing.

Julia	I suppose if it's only a week it might be OK. Have you got a garden shed?
Frankie	Yes, but it's right by the kitchen, It wouldn't be safe. Have you got anywhere?
Julia	If you'd come round to tea those times I asked you, you'd know I haven't.
Frankie	Sorry.
Julia	So there's nothing.
Frankie	Not nothing. I do know a good place for it, where the compost heap is. No one goes there. Only me. And Alf, of course … Alf! He'll help. I could

	tell him I want to keep my new pet there …
Julia	Is he that stupid old man who wears a straw hat all the time? Even when it rains? The one who does everyone's gardening?
Frankie	He's not stupid. And he keeps rabbits. He knows all about them.
Julia	But your 'thing' isn't a rabbit.
Frankie	He might have an old hutch, or he'd build a new one. Would you be able to get wood from your dad's yard?
Julia	Wood costs a lot, Frankie. You can't expect Dad to give it away. Why should he? It's not as if we're best friends is it?
Frankie	No.
	Pause.
Julia	He has got a lot of scrap. He might give some of that.
Frankie	Would you mind asking him?
Julia	You won't let Alf see the creature, will you?
Frankie	Well … I don't know.
Julia	If you do, he's bound to guess where it came from. And then he'll have to tell or he'd get into trouble.
Frankie	Alf's my friend. He'd be on my side.
Julia	I can't get the wood if we take any risks …
Frankie	All right. I won't let him see.
Julia	When can he do it?
Frankie	He comes on Saturdays. I'll ask him tomorrow.
Julia	And I'll get the wood ready. You can help carry it round.
	Frankie notices the time.
Frankie	We'd better go down to tea now. It'll be ready.
	Frankie looks down at the monster on her lap, about to lift it off.
Frankie	Wow! Weird!

Julia	Revolting!
Frankie	It's copied my hands!
Julia	Only you haven't got 300 fingers.

Frankie talks to monster as she puts it on the floor.

Frankie	Don't change any more while I'm away. Thanks for your help, Julia.
Julia	I'm glad you asked me.
Frankie	Are you?
Julia	Well, I was at first. Then, when I saw it, I wasn't. But I am now …

She looks at monster.

Sort of.

They walk off with Julia talking.

Julia I do think, though, that you're feeding it too much. Why not try four small meals a day. Small ones. Not more than ten or so grammes at a time …

Frankie and Julia exit.

Monster flexes its new shape.

Scene Eight: *The Steins' garden*

Transformation to the garden during the narration.

Narrator Frankie lives in a small town,
Where every house has a garden.
Neat gardens, rich with roses and
lavender and cats.

Enter Alf, a gardener in his 40s or 50s. He wears working clothes and a straw hat. He is weeding a flower bed.

Warm, cosy, safe world.
Can't see the lab on the hill.
The last place on earth for
A monster to be.

Enter Frankie.

She approaches Alf with purpose.

Alf Lot of weeds come up, Frankie. The storm we had a couple of nights ago, that's what done it. Lots of weeds.

Frankie Don't you ever feel like leaving them there?

Alf Don't get what you mean. Leave what here?

Frankie The weeds.

Alf They're weeds. Got to come up. This is a flower bed. Can't have weeds growing in a flower bed.

Frankie Suppose not.

Pause.

Alf Not the right place for them here.
No point them growing where they cause so much trouble.

Pause. Alf continues to work.

Frankie Alf. Can I ...

Hazel enters carrying her swimming things.

Hazel I rang the doorbell four times. Lucky the back gate was open.

Frankie is surprised, but remembers her date with Hazel at once.

Frankie Hazel!

Hazel Don't tell me you've forgotten.

Frankie Swimming!

Hazel You have forgotten!

Frankie No!

Hazel Yes, you have.

Hazel and Frankie move away from Alf who is engrossed in his work.

Frankie I've got to do something else.

Hazel You could have let me know.

Frankie I didn't have time.

Hazel Why not? What have you got to do?

Frankie I can't really tell you.

Hazel   Are you in trouble?

Frankie   Not yet.

Hazel   Yet?

Frankie   I'm just trying to sort it out at the moment.

Hazel   Do you need any help?

Frankie   Not really.

Julia enters carrying a piece of wood.

Julia   Have you spoken to him yet?

She notices Hazel and looks suspicious.

Hazel   What are you doing here?

Julia   Frankie?

Frankie   Hazel came round to go swimming.

Hazel   What's the wood for?

Frankie   Nothing special.

Julia   Something we're doing.

Hazel   I'll give you a hand, Frankie. We'll get it done dead quickly.

Julia   No thanks. We can manage. Can't we Frankie?

Hazel   You sure?

Frankie   Probably.

Hazel   So you can't come swimming?

Frankie   Not today.

Hazel   What about tomorrow?

Julia   Frankie's spending the whole day with me tomorrow.

Hazel   With you?

Julia   There won't be any time for swimming.

Frankie   I'm sorry, Hazel …

Hazel looks fed up.

Hazel   What for? You can do what you like.
You don't have to tell me about it.

Frankie   It's not that I don't want to. I just can't.

Hazel looks even more fed up.

Hazel   Can't?

Frankie   I don't have any choice.

Hazel is hurt.

Hazel   What are you on about? No choice!

Julia   We'd better get on.

Hazel   Don't worry. I won't get in your way.

Julia   Bye.

Hazel makes to go.

Frankie makes a decision and rushes up to her.

She takes her to one side, excluding Julia who watches on impatiently.

Frankie   Hazel, I'm really sorry.

Hazel   You better had be! Telling Julia Hobson instead of me!

Frankie   I thought I could trust her best of all.

Hazel   Her?

Frankie   You know how she keeps everything to herself.

Hazel   But I wouldn't tell anyone.

Frankie   Usually you do. What about at school?

Hazel   School's school. You know what it's like. Someone tells you, then you go off and tell someone else and tell them not to tell. And they do the same. But that's just little things. Not important things. I'd never tell important things.

Frankie   I thought of telling you first. I nearly phoned you.

Hazel   You should have done.

Frankie   Do you promise you won't give it away, not any of it?

Hazel   Not a word.

Frankie   And you'll help?

Hazel   No matter what.

Frankie	In face of danger?
Hazel	Danger?
Frankie	It could get that bad.
Hazel	Depends what it is.
Frankie	It's hard to describe.
Hazel	Just tell me, Frankie.
Frankie	I think it's better if I show you.
	She turns to Julia.
	Can you wait here while I take Hazel up to my room?
Julia	But she'll …
Frankie	That's why.
Julia	You can't show her now. We've got to collect all the wood by lunchtime. It won't wait around all day.
Frankie	By lunchtime!
Julia	Or it'll be taken away.
Frankie	But I haven't asked Alf yet.
	Alf, who has been immersed in his work and ignoring the girls, registers the mention of his name.
Julia	Well, you should have done. You said that you'd have it all sorted out by the time I got here. I've kept to my side of the bargain.
Hazel	Go and ask him, Frankie. Show me later.
	Frankie looks at her watch.
Frankie	I guess you'll find out soon enough.
Hazel	Can't wait.
	Hazel and Frankie laugh together. Julia isn't amused.
Julia	Go on then.
	Frankie approaches Alf.
	Hazel and Julia hover behind.

Frankie	Alf, are you very busy today?
Alf	As busy as usual.
Frankie	Would you mind fitting in another job?
Alf	What sort of job?
Frankie	Building something.

He looks at Julia's wood.

Alf	Out of wood, is it?
Frankie	A rabbit hutch.
Alf	One piece won't be enough.

Julia butts in:

Julia	We've got lots more.
Frankie	I need quite a big rabbit hutch. Will you?
Alf	It'll take more than today.
Julia	We can help.
Alf	Takes longer than you think, making it properly. When do you want it done by?
Frankie	Well, the rabbit's living in my room at the moment …
Alf	That's no place for it. Shouldn't keep it there, all closed up indoors.
Frankie	It's a surprise. I'm hiding it.
Alf	A surprise?
Frankie	For David. For his birthday.
Alf	David's birthday … I remember having a bit of his birthday cake – when was it now? After the Whitsun break. I come back from Bournemouth on the Tuesday and it was the next Saturday. May, that's when it was. Bit of a long time to plan his present for him. Nearly a year till next May.

Pause. Frankie is caught out.

Frankie	Well, I suppose … I want it for myself.
Alf	That's what I'm thinking. That's what I'm telling myself. It's Frankie who wants a pet, not her brother. All right. I'll make a hutch for you. I'll

	come round tomorrow so it's ready quick.
Julia	Brilliant!
Frankie	Thanks Alf.
Alf	Where do you want it put?
Hazel	Behind the hedge. Sort of … hidden.
Alf	So's no one can see it, huh?
Frankie	I'm not really meant to …
Alf	I understand. I'll keep your secret for you. Behind the hedge. And how big?
Frankie	It's about this size now.

Shows a rabbit sort of size with her hands.

But it's still growing. It could grow quite a lot.

Alf looks questioning.

Alf	A very big rabbit, is it? We'll need a roomy hutch. Lots of space.
Frankie	Actually, it's not quite a rabbit.
Julia	Frankie!
Frankie	It's a rare sort of creature. There aren't any others in this country. It's unusual.
Alf	Screws, then.
Frankie	Screws?
Alf	We'll use screws to build it so as no one can hear what we're doing.
Frankie	I knew you'd help.
Alf	On one condition.

Julia turns to Frankie.

| **Julia** | Told you. |
| **Alf** | Need to see it first. To make a proper home for an animal, got to know what it is. |

Julia turns to Frankie again.

Julia	Now, you've had it.
Frankie	What, this minute?
Alf	Can't do any building till I know.

Hazel	We can all go up together.
Julia	And invite the neighbours!
Alf	Bring it out here, Frankie. Give it some fresh air.
Hazel	No one's here. You wouldn't be seen.
Julia	That's not the point.
Frankie	Just bring it down?
Hazel	Go on Frankie.
Frankie	I think it'd like to. I think it would.
Alf	Get it then.
Frankie	Right. I will.

She exits.

During the narration the company pass on a large, cardboard box.

Domed head.
Still no nose,
Or hair,
Or ears.
Thin slit of a mouth.
Twenty fingers on one hand,
Two on the other.
Fleshy, thick body,
Grey-green in colour.
Short stumpy arms.
And legs
With lips on the end
Which it uses to eat its food.

Frankie places the box on the floor.

Dolphin-like sounds are heard. Frankie opens the box.

All the characters peer inside.

Hazel	It's horrible!
Julia	Yuck!
Alf	Whatever sort of animal you've got there. I don't like the look of her …
Frankie	Its name's Monnie.

Julia	Monnie?
Frankie	Names are important.
Alf	Not very healthy, are you? Can't have been good for you up in that room. Has your skin always peeled like that?
Julia	Not when I last saw it, it wasn't.
Frankie	The jelly's just wearing off.
Hazel	Jelly! Ugh!
Julia	That's what it used to be covered in.
Frankie	It isn't ill. Look how bright its eyes are. And it ate all its food, every scrap.

Alf looks into the box and seems to examine it.

Frankie	It hasn't got any spots or sores, has it?
Alf	You never said she's a water creature.
Frankie	Is she?
Alf	Don't you know?
Frankie	I just sort of found her.
Alf	Look, behind these tendrils, those slits. They're gills.

Alf's hat is knocked off.

The girls all laugh. Hazel still unsure.

Alf	Cheeky.
Frankie	I think she'll like it here.
Hazel	She's young isn't she?
Frankie	Yes.
Alf	Thought so. Has the look of a baby. I'll make the right home for her.
Frankie	Thank you, Alf, thank you.
Alf	Funny little creature.

Company create effect of Monster coming out of the box and exploring the garden.
Music.

Alf	Have a feeling she won't like being stuck here for

long. Get too big. What'll you do then Frankie?
Sound gets bigger and bigger.
Monster gets larger and larger.
All look on in amazement and horror.

Frankie   I don't know what I'll do. I don't know!

Act Two

Scene One: *The Steins' garden*

There is now a fully built hutch in the garden.

It is early evening. As the scene progresses the light gets dimmer.

An open notebook and pencil lie on the ground.

Frankie and Monnie are by the hutch.

Frankie sings into the hutch, putting Monnie to sleep.

Monnie's music harmonises with Frankie's lullaby.

Frankie … When the bough breaks the cradle will fall, Down will come baby, cradle and all.

The music turns into sleeping sounds.

Frankie hums the lullaby.

Sleeping noises are heard spasmodically throughout the scene.

Frankie sits down, picks up the notebook and concentrates.

Hazel enters.

Hazel We'll have to get another ball. Can't find it anywhere.

Frankie Shhhh.

Hazel reduces her voice to a loud whisper.

Hazel You got her to sleep!

Frankie You can always tell she's tired when her fingers droop.

Hazel Well done.

Frankie I still hate leaving her in that hutch, though.

Hazel She's getting used to it.

Frankie I'm not sure …

Hazel Think how she was today. Playing ball… well, until she lost it … picking dandelions …

Frankie	… eating dandelions …
Frankie	You shouldn't have taught her 'Waltzing Matilda'. Someone will hear.
Hazel	They'll think it's you. You've got the same sort of voice as her.
Frankie	Have I?
Hazel	All high and out of tune.
Frankie	Ha, ha, ha.

Pause.

Hazel	She's too big for your room now anyway. There's nowhere else for her to go.
Frankie	She'll soon be too big for the hutch as well. Yesterday she grew from …

She refers to the notebook.

75 centimetres to 81 centimetres.

Hazel	If she keeps on at that rate she'll be over 2 metres by the time we go back to school.
Frankie	And 4 metres by Christmas!
Hazel	We'll have to do something.
Frankie	Ben will know. He'll sort it out. Next week I can show him the record book and he'll be able to work out her rate of growth and all that.
Hazel	You've not got everything about her in there, have you.
Frankie	Only the important things. I've got to keep the notes short – that's what David's always saying. Problem is, I keep wanting to add stuff.
Hazel	Like what?
Frankie	Like what happened today. I mean, should I say that Julia cried when Alf gave Monnie all the food to eat?
Hazel	Does that count as hard, scientific fact?
Frankie	No. Just Julia losing her temper.
Hazel	So it can't go in.

Frankie looks at what she has just written.
Pause. Frankie thinks.

Frankie But, I've started writing it now.

Hazel Cross it out then.

Frankie That'll mess it up.

Hazel What have you put?

Frankie reads from her record book:

Frankie 'Day Eight. Height 81 centimetres. All jelly coating now gone. M. shows signs of intelligence, eg. guessing the flavour, imitation of birds, affection for Frances Stein, counting up to five …'

Hazel What about me and Alf! You should put in that she likes us too.

Frankie It was only an example

Hazel You can't just say she likes you.

Frankie That's what I mean about scientific notes. You can't put in everything. You've got to choose.

Hazel All right. Go on.

Frankie 'Appearance: Handsome.'

Hazel I'd say that she was 'unusual' not 'handsome'.

Frankie I think she's handsome.

Hazel But that's your opinion.

Frankie And these are my notes.

Hazel I can see that.

Frankie Shall I go on?

Hazel Sorry.

Frankie 'Growth remains rapid in spite of reduced diet. Julia Hobson accuses Frances Stein of over-feeding. Frances Stein denies this. Hazel Brent confesses she gave M. some sweets …'

Hazel Smarties to be precise.

Frankie pencils in the word 'Smarties'.

Frankie	Brackets ... 'Smarties'.
Hazel	And put that she could tell all the colours just by tasting.
Frankie	That's already in under 'guessing the flavour'.
Hazel	OK.
Frankie	' ... Animal expert Alfred Haynes gives M. a good dinner and says he's not going to starve any animal in his care. He says it's cruel and he's not having it. Frances Stein and Hazel Brent agree with him. Julia Hobson ...' That's when she started crying.
Hazel	Don't say she lost her temper. Put something else about her. Something she'll like when she reads it. Then she might be a bit nicer tomorrow and we won't have to waste time cheering her up.
Frankie	I know ...

Frankie writes as she speaks.

'Julia Hobson kindly donated this book for our record for which we are duly grateful.'

Hazel	Brilliant. That should keep her happy.

The sleeping music suddenly becomes anxious cries.

Frankie rushes to the hutch and puts her hand out as if holding Monnie's hand.

Frankie	I'm here, Monnie. I'm here.

Music relaxes.

Frankie and Hazel both hum the last two lines of the lullaby.

The sleeping music resumes.

Frankie removes her hand from the hutch and pulls away.

Frankie	Goodnight little Monnie.
Hazel	Goodnight.

Hazel and Frankie creep off.

Narrator	What are you afraid of at night, Just you, alone in the dark? What makes you toss and turn, Asleep in an unknown bed?
	Will anyone hear if you call? Will anyone help you in danger? Even a monster is scared Lying outside in the cold.

Scene Two: *The Stein home downstairs*

Frankie is carrying out a tray loaded with a variety of strange foodstuffs.

David enters and stops in front of Frankie forcing her to stop too.

David	Hello Frankie.
	He carelessly picks up the record book.
Frankie	Leave my things alone.
	David quickly puts the book down.
David	Sorry.
Frankie	What do you want?
David	You lonely or something, Frankie?
Frankie	Lonely?
David	Would you like me to take you to the zoo sometime?
Frankie	I went to the zoo last month with Katie.
David	Well, you could go again.
Frankie	Why?
David	To see the animals.
Frankie	Not why go to the zoo, stupid. Why are you asking me to go with you?
David	You're my sister, aren't you.
Frankie	We've never gone before.
David	We don't have to go to the zoo. We could go to the cinema.

Frankie	In this weather! It'd be boiling!
David	Why are you being so difficult. I'm only trying to do you a favour.
Frankie	I'm sorry. I'm just not used to it.
David	I know you might not think so, but you can talk to me, Frankie.
Frankie	What about?
David	Well, if you were in trouble or anything.
Frankie	I'd tell Ben first. You'd run down and tell Dad.
David	No I wouldn't! I wouldn't say a word to him. Not if you didn't want me to. I'm not a grass. I'm on your side.
Frankie	Thanks but I don't need any help at the moment.
David	You sure?
Frankie	Course I'm sure. Why are you so bothered all of a sudden?
David	You've been acting very oddly this last couple of weeks.
Frankie	No, I haven't.
David	Yes you have. You're always gazing into the air or rushing off. And Mrs Drake says that you've been eating a lot of leftovers from the fridge.

He looks accusingly at the tray.

Frankie	I get hungry when it's hot.
David	And why were you crying at dinner yesterday?
Frankie	I'd had a row with Julia.
David	Is that all?
Frankie	Yes.
David	Only it can be easier to confide in someone nearer your own age …
Frankie	Nearer my own age than who? I bet old Drakie put you up to this.
David	No she didn't.
Frankie	Don't lie.

David	I'm not. It wasn't her.
Frankie	Who was it then?
David	Dad.
Frankie	Dad!
David	He's worried about you.
Frankie	Dad!
David	But I wouldn't have told him if there had been anything. Honest Frankie. If he's so concerned, he should have spoken to you himself. Why should I do his dirty work? Why should I tell him anything. He can hardly be bothered to talk to me.
Frankie	I thought you got on well with him ...
David	Nothing like as well as Ben does.
Frankie	I suppose not.
David	So, you're sure that there's nothing wrong.
Frankie	I told you.
David	Right then. He can't say I didn't ask you. See you later.
	David exits.
	Frankie watches him go.
	Frankie exits.
Narrator	Responsibility means Getting the food in Cleaning up after Taking care of Watching out for Sorting problems out Planning ahead in case And not being able to stop Even if it gets too much Because everything depends on you.

Scene Three: *The Steins' garden*

Julia is waiting in the garden.
Frankie enters.
She is holding a large box containing some food.
Frankie whistles loudly to call Monnie.

Frankie	Breakfast's here!
Julia	You're down late this morning.
Frankie	My darling brother nabbed me.
Julia	Why? Is he suspicious?
Frankie	Not really.

She looks towards the hutch.

Frankie   Breakfast, Monnie!

There is no reaction from the hutch.
Frankie turns to Julia.

Have you seen her yet?

Julia   Only just got here myself. Do you like my dress?

Frankie   That the one you went to get yesterday?

She looks at the hutch again.

You're not still sleeping are you, lazy bones?

Julia   Yes, and I got two pairs of shorts, a T-shirt and a pair of jeans …

Frankie   No wonder you took so long.

Frankie approaches the hutch.

Frankie   We'll have to wake you up.

She looks inside the hutch.

Julia   And tomorrow I'm going to have my hair cut …

Frankie   Monnie? Monnie? Don't mess around!

Julia   Can't you see her then?

Frankie   What do you think!

Julia   She's probably under the straw.

Frankie gets inside the hutch to search.

Hazel enters. She is carrying a bag.
Hazel looks askance at Julia's dress.

Hazel Good morning. Frankie not down yet?

Julia She's inside the hutch.

Hazel is surprised.

Hazel Won't Monnie come out?

Julia I think she's still asleep.

Hazel Not at this time. She's usually up at dawn.

Frankie emerges from the hutch.

Frankie She's not here!

Julia You mean she got out?

Frankie Of course that's what I mean.

Julia She probably jumped over the netting.

She addresses Hazel:

I told you not to teach her to jump.

Frankie It's my fault. I forgot to ask Alf to make the run higher. We've got to find her.

Hazel She won't have gone far.

Julia She might have done.

Frankie The garden door!

Julia It was closed when I got here.

Hazel Did you shut it behind you?

Julia Course I did. Did you?

Hazel What do you think?

Frankie This is awful. Why's she so hard to look after?

Hazel We musn't panic.

Julia She can't have got out through the door.

Hazel And the wall's too high for her to climb.

Julia So she has to be here somewhere.

Frankie Monnie! Monnie!

Hazel joins in.
Hazel whistles.

Hazel   Monnie! Monnie!

They search round the garden. They have no luck.

Julia   This bit of wall isn't too high for her.

Hazel   She's right. It isn't.

Julia   What's there?

Frankie   Mrs Pritchard's. She's old and looks out of the window a lot.

Hazel   You've got to go over and search, Frankie. Monnie must be in there somewhere.

Julia   Tell Mrs Pritchard you're looking for a ball.

Frankie climbs up and looks over.

Frankie   There's so many bushes and things. It'll take me ages.

Julia   You'd better get started then.

Frankie   What if something's happened to her?

Hazel   I'm sure she's all right. You've just got to find her.

Frankie   Keep watch for me.

Frankie leaps over the wall and is gone from sight. Sounds of her landing can be heard.

Frankie   Ouch!

Hazel   What happened!

Frankie   Landed in a lavender bush.

Julia avidly keeps watch.

Julia   Shhhhh.

Hazel calls over as quietly as she can:

Hazel   What can you see?

Frankie   Trees, grass, shrubs ... It's all so overgrown.

Hazel   Just think where she'd like to go.

Julia   If we get caught my mum'll be furious with Frankie.

Hazel   Why can't you think of Monnie for a change. She might be in trouble.

Julia	I bet she isn't. I bet she thinks this is all a game. You teach her enough of them.
Hazel	And she has a very good time with me.
Julia	What's that supposed to mean?
Hazel	What it says.
Julia	She has a good time with me too.
Hazel	Well, if you …

Frankie calls out in a panic:

Frankie	Hazel! Hazel! Julia!
Hazel	What's happened!
Julia	Have you found her.
Frankie	She's in the pond … at the bottom. Her eyes are open. Wide open.

Julia speaks to Hazel:

Julia	If your eyes are open without blinking that means you're dead.
Hazel	Is she blinking?
Frankie	None of her's moving. Not her eyes. Not anything.

Julia speaks to Hazel again:

Julia	I told you she'd been looking ill these last few days.
Hazel	Can you reach her?
Frankie	Probably …

Sounds of crying are heard.

Hazel goes to her bag and takes out a towel.

Hazel	You've got to get her out Frankie.

Hazel passes the towel over the wall.

Hazel	Wrap her in this.

The towel vanishes over the wall.

Pause.

Julia	We'll have to bury her straight away. Then no one will know that this ever happened. Or I suppose we should return her to the lab. They could find out …

There is a loud high-pitched whistle followed by a splash.

Music of movement and sounds like 'Frankie'.

Frankie   Monnie!

Hazel   Sounds like the funeral's off.

Alf enters unnoticed by the girls.

Frankie   Out of there, Monnie! You'll be seen!
She's all right!

Julia   Catch her before she causes too much trouble.

Alf   Escape, did she?

Both girls jump.

Hazel   Frankie's trying to get her out of the pond.

Alf   Goes for water a lot, that creature. Needs more of it in my opinion. Stop her skin drying up so much. Like I said, she's a water creature.

Julia corrects Alf.

Julia   An amphibian.

Frankie   Please, Monnie!

Hazel   Get her!

Frankie   Got you!

Hazel   Pass her over.

Frankie   Coming up!

Two hands appear holding the towel.

Company take the towel and create the effect of monster moving under it.

Monnie bounces on to the floor and starts singing what sounds like 'Waltzing Matilda'.

Hazel and Alf laugh.

Julia   Don't encourage her.

Frankie climbs back over.

Frankie   It's not funny, Monnie. I thought you were a gonner.

Hazel   So did Julia.

Julia deliberately ignores Hazel.

Julia   You can't let her get out again. Supposing that poor old lady next door had seen her and had a heart attack.

Frankie   Alf … would you mind … I know it's a lot of trouble …

Alf   Don't mind at all, Frankie. I'll build the run higher. But can't do it forever. And she isn't going to get any smaller. Need to think about somewhere else for her.

Frankie   Ben'll know. He's back at the weekend. Just got to hang on till then.

Alf   In France isn't he?

Monnie in the towel, is bouncing back up against the wall, trying to get over it again.

Frankie   On holiday. Monnie, please don't do that.

Monnie moans and stops.

Alf   Mrs Drake took a call from him when we was having our tea. He's had an invite to stay on. Won't be back till September.

Frankie   September!

The towel starts tentatively bouncing against the wall again.

Alf   That's what she said.

Frankie   Are you sure it was Ben?

Alf   Couldn't be surer.

Frankie   But Ben's the only one! I can't look after her on my own like this for much longer. Stop, Monnie, you can't go over that wall.

Monnie moans and stops.

Hazel   We'll just have to think of a way ourselves.

Frankie   We're meant to be going on holiday in two weeks.

Julia   And I'm off next week.

Frankie   And Alf's off in the middle of the month.

Alf   Going to the Isle of Wight with my brother.

	Can't cancel now. Got the tickets and everything.

David's voice from another part of the garden.

David   Frankie!

Frankie   What does he want! I thought I'd put him off!

The towel starts bouncing against the wall again.

Julia   You could tell him. He might know what to do. He took the stuff in the first place.

David   Frankie! Where are you!

Frankie   Don't be stupid. He'd fry her for breakfast.

Hazel   I'll head him off.

She exits in the direction of the voice.

David calls from offstage.

David   Frankie! Dad's coming out to talk to you!

Frankie   Monnie! Stop that!

She grabs the towel just as it is about to disappear over the wall.

Monnie protests loudly. Frankie fights with the towel.

David   Frankie!

Frankie looks around desperately, the towel squirms.

Frankie   No! No!

Frankie throws the towel into the old cardboard box, still by the hutch.

David   Stop messing around, Frankie!

Frankie picks up the box and runs off.

David enters.

David   Where's Frankie?

Scene Four: *The street into the derelict yard*

Frankie, carrying the box, runs around the stage.

Narrator　Panic pushed Frankie through the door
Out of the garden and into the world.
Into the streets
Peopled with strangers
Whose eyes see
And ears hear
And hands touch
And tongues wag.

Frankie runs, speaking as though to passers by.

Frankie　It's my dog. She's got the flu.

Narrator　So many dangers:
Children playing,
Woman shopping,
Man phoning,
Men talking,
Dog trotting,
Women queuing.

Frankie　My labrador ... I'm worried about her ... Got to get to the vet.

Narrator　Stop running.
Musn't cry.
Hide the fear.
Act relaxed.
Got to be normal
Like everyone else,
Fit in quickly
Or be found out.

Hazel catches up with Frankie.

They quickly dart into an empty space signifying a derelict yard.

Sounds of Monnie's music with a whimpering quality are heard.

Hazel　You can't half run fast sometimes!

Frankie　David was coming.

Monnie's music.

Frankie comforts Monnie still in the box:

Frankie   Don't worry, Monnie. We're safe, I promise, we're safe.

Hazel   He followed you out the garden door too. Lost him now, though.

More whimpering. Frankie struggles to control the box, calming Monnie.

Frankie   Just stay still. As still as you can.

She turns to Hazel.

Did he hear me go?

Hazel   Only him and the rest of the universe! You made some racket!

Frankie   I couldn't stay there.

Whimpering music .

Hazel   Where can we go that's safe?

Whimpering music.

Frankie   I think she needs some water.

Hazel   If you head home, David'll get you. He's on the look out now.

Frankie   Is your mum in?

Hazel   What time is it?

Frankie   10.30.

Hazel   She'll be home at two.

Frankie   So we could hide Monnie at yours until the coast's clear …

Hazel   And then sneak her back later.

Whimpering music.

Frankie   Come on!

They start to go.

Hazel stops hard in her tracks.

Hazel   Knickers!

Frankie   What?

Hazel	My key's in my bag.
Frankie	And your bag's in the garden.
Hazel	Your garden.
Frankie	Double knickers!
Hazel	I'll go and get the key. You wait here.

Whimpering music as if in response to Hazel's leaving.

Frankie	How long will you be?
Hazel	No time.

She speaks to Monnie:

Don't worry, Monnie, I'll be quick.

She turns her attention back to Frankie.

I'll tell David and Mrs Drake that you're coming to mine for lunch.

Frankie	Try to stop Julia from inviting herself over.
Hazel	Some hope!
Frankie	Please.
Hazel	See you soon.

Whimpering music.

Hazel speaks to Monnie:

Very soon.

Hazel exits.

Frankie sits tensely, keeping a constant look out.

Monnie's music changes pitch, like a demand.

Monnie	Water!
Frankie	There isn't a tap or anything here, Monnie. You'll have to wait till we get to Hazel's. She's got a shower. You can try that.

Monnie whistles.

Frankie	All right then. But stay near me. Promise?

Music seems to contain the word …

Monnie	Promise.

The box put down. Company create effect of

Monnie getting out of box and exploring the new environment.

Frankie We're not in the garden anymore.

Monnie comes back and gently rests against Frankie's leg.

Frankie strokes her.

Narrator Being peculiar,
A fish out of water,
Was all Monnie knew
Since the day she was born.

She thought it was
Normal to seem out of place;
Normal to look, move and speak
Differently, weirdly, oddly;
Normal to be at the mercy of
Creatures who were
Nothing like her.

Scene Five: *The Steins' garden*

Alf and Julia are clearing out the hutch.

Julia Do you always go to the Isle of Wight for your holiday then?

Alf Every other year I do, yes.

Julia Doesn't it get a bit boring going to the same place all the time?

Alf I wouldn't keep going if I found it boring, now would I? Anyways, I visit Cornwall the years in between ...

Julia I went to Gibraltar last year ...

Enter Hazel, looking around carefully.

Hazel He gone then?

Julia Who?

Hazel David, of course.

Julia He was hardly here. Don't know why Frankie had to make such a fuss about him. If she'd been sensible ...

Hazel   What did he say about the screaming?

Julia   He asked what stupid game we were playing. He's very rude, isn't he? I'm not surprised she hates him.

Alf   Tell her she can bring Monnie back now. Coast is clear.

Hazel   Did he see the hutch?

Alf   Didn't bother about it. Thinks it's for rabbits.

Julia goes to the gate to look out.

Julia   Where are they anyway?

Hazel   Hiding in an alleyway.

Julia   An alleyway!

Hazel   Off Low street.

Julia   That's miles away!

Hazel   Frankie's a good runner.

Julia   She's off her head going so far.

Hazel   She was scared. Everyone runs for it when they're scared.

Julia   She's bound to get caught now.

Hazel   Don't see why. They're well hidden.

Julia   You really don't think about things properly do you?

Hazel   Yes I do. We've got a plan to get Monnie back here.

Julia   Well I've had enough of this. I really have! You two with your plans and ideas! Things are always going wrong. Each time it gets worse and worse!

Hazel   You don't have to hang around if you don't want to. We can manage fine without you, you know!

Julia   Frankie told me first. We were doing very well before you poked your nose in.

Hazel   I didn't poke my nose in.

Julia   Well, it looked like it to me.

Alf tries to calm things down:

Alf	What's the plan, Hazel?
Julia	Yes. You'd better tell us.
Hazel	Why are you so bothered? You don't even like Monnie?
Julia	How can anyone like something that's so dangerous.
Hazel	I'm not telling you the plan if you don't care about Monnie.
Alf	Tell me then …
Julia	No. I don't care! I don't! And I'm fed up of risking my neck and being used by you and Frankie. You're both liars!
Alf	Hold on a minute …
Julia	I bet she knew that Ben wasn't coming back. She only said that to make me help her!
Hazel	No. She didn't.
Julia	Well, you'll all go to prison. All of you! And I'm not going with you!

Julia sets off purposefully.

Hazel	Where are you off to?
Julia	To do what Frankie should have done in the first place!
Alf	What's that?
Julia	Tell Professor Stein.
Hazel	You can't!
Julia	I can and I am!

Hazel leaps at Julia and catches hold of her dress.

Julia jerks away and the dress rips.

Julia screams and screams. She clutches her dress and seems paralysed.

Hazel	Alf. Make her be quiet.
Alf	I think you'd better go home, Julia. Try to get that dress fixed.

Prof. Stein calls from offstage.

Prof. Stein Frances! Are you all right?

Hazel shouts back to him:

Hazel We're just playing.

Enter Prof. Stein.

Prof. Stein Frances?

Julia runs up to him.

Julia She's gone. She's taken her monster with her and she's gone.

Prof. Stein You are ...?

Julia Julia. Julia Hobson.

Prof. Stein Come along with me ...

He has forgotten her name.

Julia Julia.

Prof. Stein Julia. Tell me where Frances is and what she is doing with a monster.

Prof. Stein ushers Julia off.

Alf joins Prof. Stein as he exits.

Scene Six: *The alley*

Narrator Monnie, at the mercy of creatures
So different to her,
And dreaming, such dreaming
Of what her webs and gills,
Skin and fins could do
If she left the land behind
And plunged into a new world,
A wet world,
Lots of space,
Hidden depths;
Gravity losing hold,
Other creatures whistling,
Swimming, breathing, like her,
Just like her.

Hazel and Frankie in very urgent mid-
conversation. The company use the towel to create
the effect of Monnie moving around the alley.

Hazel   ... Now he knows everything, the whole story.

Frankie   Does he know where we are?

Hazel   No, no. I got out as soon as I could. Alf's talking
              to him.

Frankie   I can't go back. They'll get me.

Hazel   They'll get Monnie too.

Frankie   I hate Julia! I'm glad you tore her dress.

Hazel   I would've ...

Sounds of a van pulling up nearby.

Both girls duck down.

Monnie moves forward to look but is pulled back.

Frankie   Did she see us?

Hazel   No.

She cranes her neck to see more clearly.

              She's gone into the house. Delivering something.
              It's just a van from Didon Nurseries. She won't be
              looking for us.

Frankie   Has she locked the door?

Hazel   Frankie! Are you mad? We can't steal a van.
              We don't know how to drive.

Frankie   Not steal it, pea brain. Hitch a lift.

Hazel   Where to?

Frankie   Out of here. To Didon. Near the Creek.
              Monnie can go in the sea. She needs the water ...

Hazel   ... and there's the old house by the field. No
              one'll find her in there.

Frankie stands up.

Frankie   The back's open. If there's something I can hide
              under ...

Hazel   What do you mean 'I'?

Frankie   Well, me and Monnie.

Hazel	What about me?
Frankie	It's too dangerous for all of us to go. I've got you in enough trouble already.
Hazel	But you can't go there on your own.
Frankie	Monnie'll be with me. You've got to cover.
Hazel	I don't know what to say.
Frankie	Say I've gone to the pictures … tell them anything. I'll make sure Monnie's safe, then I'll come back by bus.
Hazel	What if the van isn't going to Didon.
Frankie	It's bound to get there in the end. Keep a watch out will you.

She puts the towel and Monnie back into the box, gets up and goes off towards the van.

Hazel moves to follow her, then checks herself.

She opens her mouth to call out, then stops.

Pause. The van engine starts up again.

Hazel	I hope she's got enough for the bus fare home.

Scene Seven: *The meadow by the Creek*

Narrator	The Creek lies hidden Behind the summer house Before the hill Beyond the meadow leading down to the sea. And around this meadow is a large, brown fence Marked by a sign saying Private.

Private places are best for monsters.

Frankie runs in holding the box.

Frankie	Made it! Made it! Didon meadow!

Company use towel to create effect of Monnie jumping out of the box.

Your new home.

Monnie/towel bounces around. Gleeful music.

Good isn't it.

Monnie/towel bounces then pauses and hovers as if about to jump.

Frankie   Jump over it, Monnie! Go on! Jump!

Monnie/towel leaps.

'Wheee' music turning into tumbling over.

Frankie   Fell over! Fell over!

Monnie/towel rolls over to Frankie and knocks her over too.

Aaaaaagh!

Monnie screams in harmony with Frankie:

Monnie   Aaaagh!

They both roll around and on the floor, then leap about.

Frankie   It's all yours! All of it! All of it! All of it!

Monnie's music harmonises/echoes Frankie.

No more sneaking about! No more keeping quiet! Noisy as you like!

Monnie/towel leaps about and music echoes noisily.

Frankie stops to catch her breath.

Frankie   We should have thought of coming here before.
They'll never get you now.
Not in a zillion years …

Whoops of joy and more bouncing from Monnie/towel.

Frankie is suddenly concerned.

Careful, there's a rock behind you!

Thud and squeal.

Get up Monnie, you didn't fall far.
You'll just have to learn to take more care.
Especially when I'm not around. I won't be here all the time, you know.

Monnie/towel gets up, moans and clings to Frankie's leg for comfort.

Frankie strokes Monnie.

Frankie   How can I leave you on your own! You're far too
young, aren't you. I'll have to stay here. Run
away for good. We can live off berries and things.
And when there aren't berries, we'll have to steal
carrots and lettuces from the cottage gardens
and suck milk from the cows.
(*Pause*) Don't really fancy that. (*Pause*) Not at all.
(*Pause*) Monnie, you'll just have to be one of
those creatures who grows up very quickly. I
know, let's go down to the Creek. I want to show
you the sea!

Frankie moves away from Monnie.

It's down here. Stay by that tree. I'm going to
check that the way's clear.

Frankie exits

Monnie/towel alone on stage. Music.

Two children are heard from offstage:

Child 1   It's near there!

Child 2   This way! This way!

Four children run on. They are carrying sticks.

*They stand at a distance from, but looking at
Monnie.*

Music stops. Monnie shrinks back.

Child 2   Here it is!

Child 1   Got you!

Child 3 is afraid.

Child 3   That's not an animal. I know it's not.

Child 4   I seen one of them in the zoo.

Child 2   No you ain't. There's nothing like that in the zoo.

Child 1   Nothing like it anywhere.

Child 2   It's an alien. Dropped from the sky.

Child 3   An alien!

Child 1   Monster from outer space.

Child 2   Like in the films. Like ET.

Child 1 talks to Monnie:

Child 1   Want to go home, then, do you?

Silence.

Child 4   ET was nice. Perhaps this one's nice.

Child 3   Doesn't look nice to me.

Child 2   Look how red its eyes are. It's nasty.

Child 1 starts to creep towards Monnie.
Monnie shrinks back.

Child 4   Don't go near it!

Child 2   Frightened it'll bite?

Child 1 waves his/her stick menacingly.

Child 1   If it bites, I'll show it!

Child 1 pulls off towel with the stick leaving
Company to create effect of Monnie uncovered.

Child 2   I'll show it too. Good and proper.

Child 1 points at Monnie with her stick.

Child 1   Ugly little beast, ain't you.

Child 2   Ugly as dirt.

Child 3   Look at it's feet! Like a duck's.

Child 4   And all those fingers.

Child 1 talks to Monnie again:

Child 1   Too many fingers for your own good.

Child 4   What's it made of?

Child 1   Ask it then.

Child 4 questions Monnie:

Child 4   What are you made of?

Child 2 joins in:

Child 2   Can't you talk?

Child 3   Probably speaks another language.

Child 1   Or maybe it just doesn't like us.

Child 2   I don't like it. It's spooky.

Child 3   It could've come down first. To see what it's like here. Then they'll know where to invade.

Child 4   Who'll know?

Child 3   The others.

Child 4   What others?

Child 3   The rest of the aliens. Up in their space ship.

Child 1   Hundreds of them. All like this one.

Child 2 talks to Monnie again, poking a stick in her direction.

Child 2   Think you can take over our planet do you? Think you can come here with your funny face and sus us out?

Child 1   You got no right to come here like this. No right!

Child 3   Go away, funny face! Go away!

All   Go away, funny face! Go away, funny face! Go away, funny face! Go away, funny ......

Burst of high-pitched, scream-like music .

The shouting stops.

Child 1   Get it!

All the children charge at Monnie with their sticks. They shout, scream and are out of control.

Desperate music.

Frankie enters.

She runs between the children and Monnie.

Frankie   No! Stop it! Stop it!

Tussle between Frankie and Child 1.

Frankie falls down.

Monnie whizzes off stage.

Frankie gets up and looks around.

Frankie   Where's Monnie! Where's she gone? What've you done with her?

Child 1   Keep away from that thing. It could hurt you.

Child 2   It could kill you easy. Never seen anything like it. Horrible.

Child 3	It was a monster from another planet.
Child 2	It was going for us. We had to chase it off.
Child 1	We've got to get it now. Set the dogs on it. It's dangerous, a thing like that.
Frankie	She isn't! She isn't dangerous! I'll kill you if you've hurt her.
Child 2	Is it yours then?
Frankie	Yes. Where did she go?
Child 3	What is it then?
Frankie	She's a baby. She's only a baby. You'll go to prison if she dies. Where did she go?
	Children group together and talk amongst themselves.
Frankie	Where did she go?
	Children start to move away in retreat then run off quickly.
	Child 4 stays behind and hovers.
Child 4	I wasn't in on it. I didn't do nothing.
Frankie	Did you see where Monnie went?
Child 4	Monnie? Is that her name?
Frankie	Yes.
Child 4	Short for Monica, is it?
Frankie	Sort of. Did you see which way she went?
Child 4	I got a cousin called Monica.
Frankie	Have you? Look. It's very important. Did you see which way she went?
Child 4	I saw her. Saw her running. Never touched her..
Frankie	I'm sure you didn't. Where did she go?
	Child 4 points ahead.
Child 4	Under that gate.
Frankie	There's no room.
Child 4	She squeezed herself.
	Frankie runs in direction of gate.

Child 4 runs after her.

Child 4 I'll help you!

Frankie You'd only frighten her.

Child 4 I never hurt her. It wasn't me.

Frankie I know. She's just scared of strangers. Go on. Get off home.

Child hovers.

Frankie Go on!

Child exits.

Frankie runs from one place to the next in search of Monnie.

Frankie Monnie! Monnie! It's OK, Monnie! They've gone! It's safe now! No one's going to get you! It's me, Frankie! Don't be afraid! Where are you! Monnie! Monnie! Over here!

As she runs, the green of the set becomes the blue of the sea.

Over here! I've made them go away! You can come back now! You've got to come back! You've got to! Just make a sound! Show me where you are!

Distant whistling sound from the direction of the sea.

Monnie! I'm here! I'm here! Swim back to the shore! I'm here! It goes on for ever out there! Come back! Come back!

Frankie takes off her shoes and starts to wade in.

Owwwwww, it's freezing. Owww! You can't stay in!

I'm coming to find you! Whistle again! I need to know where you are!

Now she is swimming.

Monnie! Monnie! Mustn't go too far out! ... Not safe ... Monnie!

She's getting weaker, gasping for breath.

Can't see ... Monnie ... Too deep.

The company create effect of Frankie being tossed by the sea.

Narrator Such a deep sea,
Too far from the land,
Arms and legs heavy,
Breath growing short,
Pain in her side.
Chances are slim,
Survival not likely.

Frankie passes out.

As she does so, she is supported by the company.

Monnie's music.

But, as she runs out of air
And loses her senses,
Body gone limp
Hands icy to touch,
Something strong and alive
Comes underneath
Pushing her up
Moving her along
Towards the shore
Towards safety.
The tables are turned:
The one she created
Is now looking after her.

Frankie is carefully placed on the floor. She is coughing and hardly conscious.

Some flowers are placed on Frankie's chest.

Prof. Stein enters and sees Frankie. He picks her up and carries her over to her bedroom.

A hand, a gentle hand
Strokes her face.
Just a hand on her face,
while she sleeps.

Scene Eight: *Frankie's Bedroom*

Frankie is lying in bed. She is still asleep.

Prof. Stein is sitting on the bed looking at her.
His hand is on her forehead.
Pause.
Frankie begins to stir. She registers where she is.
She looks at her father.

Prof. Stein Hello Frances.

Frankie Hello.

Prof. Stein How are you feeling?

Frankie Strange.

Prof. Stein Are you warm enough?

Frankie Yes, thanks.

Prof. Stein How's your knee?

Frankie My knee?

Prof. Stein You cut it.

Frankie bends over to feel for knee under the covers.

Frankie Ouch!

She clutches her side.

Prof. Stein Some bruised ribs too.

Prof. Stein puts his hand on her forehead.

Prof. Stein No temperature.

Frankie suddenly remembers something and looks around.

Frankie Where are they?

Prof. Stein They?

Frankie Flowers. I remember some flowers.

Prof. Stein I haven't seen any.

Frankie In my hand.

Prof. Stein When, Frances?

Frankie By the sea.

Prof. Stein They must have fallen.

Frankie So I've lost them! No!

Prof. Stein	I wasn't thinking about flowers when I picked you up.
Frankie	You picked me up?
Prof. Stein	It was fortunate that your friend knew exactly where you'd be.
Frankie	She told you?
Prof. Stein	She realised that she had to.
Frankie	You came to get me?
Prof. Stein	Of course I did. Straight away.
	Pause.
Frankie	I'm sorry.
Prof. Stein	Don't look so alarmed, Frances. I'm not going to tell you off.
Frankie	No?
Prof. Stein	I blame myself. I blame myself entirely. I didn't realise how unhappy you were.
Frankie	Unhappy?
	Pause.
Prof. Stein	Sometimes it helps to talk to someone. I know it isn't always easy. But things can grow out of all proportion if you keep them to yourself. I was just the same. It was never very easy to talk to my parents. I used to think that when I had children, I'd manage better. *(Pause)* I daresay that I haven't done very well.
Frankie	I suppose not.
Prof. Stein	I'm sorry, Frances.
	Frankie mumbles:
Frankie	So am I.
	Pause.
Frankie	Did you see the hutch?
Prof. Stein	I did.
Frankie	And you're not cross.

Prof. Stein	Cross? Frances, I have no objection to your keeping pet rabbits.
Frankie	Rabbits?
Prof. Stein	Alf informed me that it was built to house rabbits. Do you have something else in mind?
Frankie	Oh no. No.
Prof. Stein	You needn't have been so frightened of asking me before. I'm not an ogre am I?
Frankie	I thought …
Prof. Stein	It's probably very good for children to keep pets.
Frankie	As long as they don't grow too big.
Prof. Stein	Why should a rabbit grow too big?
Frankie	Oh … I was thinking of something else.
	Pause.
Prof. Stein	I'm also concerned about this 'Monsters' business.
Frankie	Monsters?
Prof. Stein	The other children teasing you at school about what we do in the laboratories.
Frankie	They've always done that.
Prof. Stein	I really should have realised that it would worry you. I ought to have explained … How much do you know about my work?
Frankie	A bit.
Prof. Stein	Well, you tell them next time that we have nothing to do with making monsters. We're concerned with finding out how plants and animals are 'put together', what makes them what they are.
Frankie	Why?
Prof. Stein	To improve crops, livestock, medicines. For people's good.
Frankie	That's dangerous, isn't it?
Prof. Stein	In what way, Frances?

Frankie	Well, you know … messing about with nature.
Prof. Stein	We research under very controlled conditions. We take special care not to let things get out of hand. One has to be very responsible in this line of work.
Frankie	But things must go wrong sometimes.
Prof. Stein	Not in any serious way. No.
Frankie	How can you be sure?
Prof. Stein	Everything is carefully watched over – I'm sure of that. Look, I think we ought to continue this conversation at another time. Your friends are outside waiting to see you. Would you like me to let them in?
Frankie	Is it Hazel?
Prof. Stein	With Alf and another girl.
Frankie	Not Julia?
Prof. Stein	I think that's her name. Yes.
Frankie	Yes. I'd like to see them.

Prof. Stein prepares to exit.

Prof. Stein	Try not to spend too long with them today.

Prof. Stein ushers in Hazel and Alf. Julia follows.

Alf hands Frankie a box of chocolates.

Frankie begins to open them.

They stand and look at Frankie until Prof. Stein has gone.

Hazel	How are you?
Frankie	Sore.
Hazel	I'm sorry I told him. I had to. It was getting dark. You could've been murdered.
Julia	You shouldn't have run away like that in the first …

Hazel gives her a warning look.

Alf	Never seen your father so worried.
Frankie	Was he?

Hazel   Frantic.

Alf   All of us were.

Hazel   Thought I wouldn't see you again.

Frankie   I'm glad I'm back.

Pause.

Frankie   Dad isn't cross with me.

Alf   Glad you're safe, isn't he.

Frankie   But I thought he'd be cross about Monnie.

Hazel   He must have believed your story Alf.

Frankie   What story?

Alf   Had to think on me feet, what with Julia rattling away ...

Julia   I'm sorry, Frankie. But I only did what I thought was right ...

Alf deliberately interrupts:

Alf   Told him it was all by way of a trick gone wrong.

Hazel   That I put a frog in a paper bag and pretended it was a monster.

Alf   Only when it hopped down the garden this one ...

Alf points at Julia.

... was so fooled she believed in it ...

Hazel   And went to tell your father because she was scared.

Alf   ... and you went running off in a rage on account of being fed up with monster jokes what with teasing at school 'bout your father working at the labs.

Hazel   And later on he asked me what might be bothering you so I told him how they call you 'Frankenstein'.

Alf   Don't think he heard half of what Julia said, anyway. That upset she was.

Julia   Adults always believe each other before they'll believe one of us.

Hazel	Specially if it's about something as unreal as monsters.
Julia	And you needn't worry about my dress. Mum managed to fix it.
Frankie	Have a chocolate Julia.
	Pause as they eat.
Hazel	Where's Monnie.
Frankie	Don't know.
Julia	How do you mean?
Frankie	She ran away.
Hazel	Not from you!
Frankie	No. From these kids. They had sticks. They really hated her. I chased them off. But she was terrified. There was no stopping her. I think she's in the sea now. I went in to get her … and then … I don't remember much … I think she saved me. We should go back to find her.
Hazel	I reckon you should leave her to it.
Frankie	To what?
Hazel	To the sea.
Frankie	How can I?
Hazel	What else can you do?
Julia	She's too big to live here.
Hazel	And she loves the water.
Alf	Sea's the best place for her. No one'll get her there.
Frankie	But they might. What about the people who kill whales. And she's never had to get food before. She doesn't know how to look after herself.
Hazel	She'll learn. Look how quickly she worked out what we were saying and how to sing 'Waltzing Matilda' …
Julia	And how to get over the wall.
Frankie	But I want to see her again.

Alf   P'raps you will, p'raps you won't. Not up to you any more, Frankie.

Frankie   It all seems like it was made up now. Like she didn't really happen. As if it's all in my head.

Hazel   Only it isn't, 'coz we knew her too.

Scene changes back into the Creek as Narrator speaks.

Narrator   There's always a hope,
When someone has gone,
That one day they will return.
And if a bird whistles behind a hedge
Or a blue ball rolls on the grass
Or a gentle hand is held,
Then for a moment,
Just a moment,
Maybe they are here.
Here again, a lost soul restored.
Even if life changes and time goes on.

Scene Nine: *The Creek*

The sound of waves and gulls.

It is the last day of the summer holidays

Frankie   Last day of the summer holidays!

Hazel   Last day of freedom!

Frankie   After today, no more swimming and sailing and lying in bed in the morning if we feel like it.

Hazel   Secondary school.

Frankie   First years.

They are both nervous.

Both   Ugh!

Hazel   Get the flowers then.

Frankie picks up the flowers.

Frankie   Here.

Hazel   And you're sure that this is the place where she left you?

Frankie	Pretty sure. Yes. This is it.
Hazel	OK. Let's do it.
Frankie	Shall I place the flowers first or say the message?
Hazel	Place the flowers.
	Frankie places the flowers on the ground.
Frankie	Right. Done it. Now for the message. 'Monnie, wherever you are, we miss you and will always think of you. Goodbye forever.'
Hazel	Goodbye.
Frankie	When the tide comes in it will wash the flowers away.
Hazel	They could end up in France.
Frankie	Or Holland. Depends on the current.
Hazel	Or maybe Monnie'll get them.
	Frankie looks sad.
Frankie	She's not here any more.
	Hazel deliberately changes the subject:
Hazel	Look. The horizon. How far away do you think it is?
Frankie	As far as my chances of getting back those sunglasses I lent you.
Hazel	No, really. How far?
Frankie	There's probably some mathematical way of working it out.
Hazel	But you don't know it.
Frankie	And neither do you.
	Hazel suddenly notices something in the sea.
Hazel	Frankie, look!
Frankie	What?
Hazel	It's the dolphin! Look! Leaping up over there!
Frankie	Where?
Hazel	That way!
Frankie	I can't see anything.

Hazel	Wait. It's under the water. Look! Now! There it is!
Frankie	Yes! You're right!
Hazel	Look at it go! There it goes again!
Frankie	It's coming closer.
Hazel	We should swim out to it.
Frankie	I'm not going in there!
Hazel	Come on! It'll be brilliant.
Frankie	Wait!
Hazel	What?
Frankie	That's not a dolphin.
Hazel	What do you mean?
Frankie	It's too big and it's swimming in the wrong way.
Hazel	And dolphins don't come this close into the shore.

Frankie and Hazel stand and watch in amazement.

A light starts to shine, growing bigger and bigger.

Company create striking, huge image of grown monster as they narrate the following:

Narrator	Suddenly! A splash of water against the rocks. Something gleaming in the sea. Something large, shining, alive. Again a splash. Again a movement. And then a whoosh of water. Spray filling the air And there, standing there Tall and high Stretching, glittering, towering …

The light is enormous, covering the whole stage.

Frankie	Monnie!

Dolphin-like music.

Narrator	Grown and adult and free!
Hazel	It's Monnie! She's here! She is!
Frankie	I thought that I'd never see her again.

Hazel	I can't believe it!
Frankie	She's grown so big!
Hazel	She's amazing! You couldn't possibly have kept her in your garden.

Frankie shouts out to Monnie:

Frankie	You're beautiful! Monnie, you're so beautiful! Look at your hands! Look at your shining hands!

Whale-like music croons.

Hazel	Where have you been?
Frankie	Are you happy?
Hazel	Have you found any friends?
Frankie	You've learnt another language!
Hazel	Do you live out there?
Frankie	Do you miss us, Monnie?
Hazel	I'm so glad that you came back!

Whale-like music says farewell.

Loud splashing.

Hazel	She's going.
Frankie	Don't go yet! Stay for longer!

Splashing recedes.

Frankie	Come back! Come back!
Hazel	Goodbye! Good luck!

Waves and gulls as before.

Hazel	She's alive, Frankie.
Frankie	Yes, she's alive.
Hazel	And she remembered us. She wanted to see us.
Frankie	Yes, she did. She remembered us. I don't think that she'll ever forget.

Fade up waves, gulls and distant whale sounds.

Narrator	What tales will she carry Back to the Dolphins? Will she tell of a hutch In a neat, green garden?

Will she sing of a girl
Who should have known better
But didn't and loved her
then set her free.

Questions and Explorations

1 Keeping Track

Act One

Scene One: The Creek

1   What difference do you think it would make to this scene if the narrator's first few lines were not there?

2   In groups of four to five
a) Write down a list of all the comments which the children at school might make to Frankie about her name.

b) Act out a scene showing how Frankie deals with this name-calling. Include Hazel in this scene and show what she does when the name-calling happens.

3   a) Draw a picture of the Creek.
b) Write a paragraph which describes the Creek as it would be presented in a tourist guide book.

4   Why is Frankie in such a bad mood? Why does she take it out on Hazel?

5   In what ways does Hazel react to Frankie's bad mood?

6   a) Imagine that you are Frankie. Write a few sentences about how you feel about Hazel, starting: 'Hazel is my friend because...'

b) Imagine that you are Hazel. Write a few sentences about your feelings for Frankie, starting: 'Frankie is my friend because ...'

7   What reasons might Professor Stein have for taking David and not Frankie to the laboratory? What do you think about him doing this?

Scene Two: The Stein home downstairs into David's bedroom

1   a) How does David treat Frankie?
    b) How does Professor Stein treat Frankie?
    c) Why do you think they both treat her in this way?

2   a) Imagine that you are Frankie. Write a letter to the problem page of your favourite magazine about the difficulties you face in your family.
    b) Imagine that you are an Agony Aunt at the magazine and write a reply to Frankie's letter giving her advice on how to deal with her situation.

3   Why does David tell Frankie to mind her own business?

4   In pairs, act out what would have happened if Professor Stein had caught David whilst stealing the 'stuff' from the laboratory.

5   a) List all the words and phrases in the scene used to describe the stolen 'stuff' in the test tube.
    b) Write a sentence or two in your own words describing what you think it is.

6   a) Give at least three reasons why Frankie *should not* take the 'stuff' from David.
    b) Give at least three good reasons why Frankie *wants* to take the 'stuff'.

Scene Three: Frankie's Bedroom

1   a) Write a list of all the feelings and pictures which thunderstorms bring up for you.
    b) Use this list to help you to write a poem about a thunder storm which has a great effect on somebody.

2 a) Draw a picture of Frankie's experiment before the thunderstorm.
b) Draw a picture of Frankie's experiment immediately after the thunderstorm.

3 What is a monster?

4 In groups of three, use drama to create the monster, showing it from the moment it is created to Frankie first seeing it.

5 List all the feelings Frankie has when she first sees the monster.

Scene Four: The Stein home downstairs into Frankie's bedroom

1 What has become of David's experiment? Why do you think this happened?

2 What differences are there between David's and Frankie's attitudes towards their experiments?

3 Frankie has a nightmare about what David and the other 'scientists' do to her monster. In groups of three, act out her very worst fears in a nightmarish way.

4 If Frankie wishes that the monster were dead, why isn't she prepared to kill it?

5 What is happening to the monster when it seems to be wrapped up in cling-film?

6 List all the feelings that Frankie has when the monster comes out of its 'cocoon'.

Scene Five, Six, and Seven: Frankie's bedroom

1 a) What sort of monsters do the narrations at the beginning of these scenes make you think of?
   b) Write a lullaby reassuring a baby that she\he is safe from monster(s) she\he fears.

2 a) What happens when Julia first touches the monster?
   b) What happens when Frankie first touches the monster?

3 What does Julia want Frankie to do with the monster?

4 What is Julia's overall attitude towards the monster?

5 In groups of four, act out of a scene showing Julia at home with her family which tells us more about what Julia is like and gives some explanation for it.

6 a) Is Frankie right to tell Julia about the monster?
   b) Why does she tell her?

7 How does Julia help Frankie?

8 Imagine that you are Frankie. Write your diary after Julia has left – show what you feel about the monster and Julia, and what you plan to do next.

Scene Eight: The Steins' garden

1 Why has Frankie forgotten about swimming with Hazel?

2 Why is Frankie keeping the monster a secret from Hazel?

3 Why doesn't Julia want Frankie to tell anyone else about the monster?

4 a) Write a few sentences about a time when it would be good for someone to keep a secret.

b) Write a few sentences about a time when it would be bad for someone to keep a secret.

5 a) Draw a picture of Alf.
   b) Why does he agree to help Frankie?

6 Draw a picture of what the monster looks like from the description of this scene.

7 What is the monster's name and how does Frankie choose it?

8 What more do you learn about the monster from Alf?

9 Write a description of the garden as seen by the monster for the very first time.

Act Two

Scene One: The Steins' garden

1 Why is Frankie keeping a record book?

2 a) Write a description of your classroom in purely factual terms.
   b) Write a description of your classroom showing what you think and feel about it.
   c) Find out what the words 'objective' and 'subjective' mean.

3 How 'objective' is Frankie being about Monnie? Back up your answer by quoting what Frankie says.

4 Imagine that you are Julia. Write up your diary entry describing how you feel about the situation with Monnie, Hazel, Frankie and Alf so far.

Scene Two: The Stein home downstairs

1   Why does Professor Stein ask David to talk to Frankie rather than doing it himself?

2   In groups of three, act out a scene showing how Frankie, David and Professor Stein would deal with the situation if their car broke down in the middle of nowhere.

3   List any ways in which David behaves differently towards Frankie in this scene.

4   Do you think that David means it when he says that Frankie can trust him? Give reasons for your answer.

5   Imagine that you are Professor Stein. Write a list of what matters most to you in your life at the moment – put each thing in order of importance. What responsibilities do you have?

Scene Three: The Steins' garden

1   Why is Monnie 'so hard to look after'?

2   What does Monnie do in this scene? Why does she do it?

3   How do Julia, Frankie and Hazel each react to the fact that Monnie is found lying stock-still at the bottom of the pond?

4   Imagine that you are Monnie lying at the bottom of the pond. Write a paragraph about what you are thinking and feeling.

5   Why do you think that Professor Stein wants to see Frankie?

6   Who is Ben and why does it matter so much to Frankie that he's not coming back from his holidays until September?

7   In groups of five or six, act out what would have happened if Frankie had not been able to run away from the garden.

Scene Four: The street into the derelict yard

1   What do Hazel and Frankie plan to do next?

2   Where do you think would be the ideal place for Monnie to live?

Scene Five: The Steins' garden

1   a) How does Julia's dress get to be torn?
    b) Whose fault is it that the dress is torn? Why?

2   Why does Julia tell Professor Stein about the monster?

Scene Six: The alley

1   Why does Frankie decide to 'hitch a lift'?

2   Where is Frankie taking Monnie?

3   Why does Frankie not let Hazel come with her?

4   Imagine that you are Hazel. Write your diary entry for that day after you have left Frankie to hitch the lift on her own – describe how you are feeling and how you think things might turn out.

Scene Seven: The meadow by the Creek

1   Draw a map of the Creek and meadow area. Mark on it the road, the fence, the summerhouse, the path to the Creek and anything else that you think is important.

2   What is Monnie's reaction to being in the meadow?

3   How do the four children react to Monnie?

4   How does Monnie react to the four children?

5   In groups of four or five, act out a situation in which people react in very different ways to a stranger coming into their midst.

6   What has happened to Frankie and Monnie by the end of this scene?

Scene Eight: Frankie's bedroom

1   Why isn't Professor Stein angry with Frankie?

2   Why is Frankie upset that the flowers that were in her hand have gone?

3   How much does Professor Stein know about Monnie?

4   What more do you learn from this scene about Professor Stein's work?

5   How right is Professor Stein when he says that things do not go wrong in any serious way in his laboratory?

6   In groups of four or five, act out a scene which shows how, 'Adults always believe each other before they'll believe one of us.'

7   In pairs, choose who will be A and B. A is the part of Frankie that would do anything to find Monnie again. B is the part that thinks it is best to forget about Monnie. A and B argue about what Frankie should do next.

Scene Nine: The Creek

1   How do Frankie and Hazel seem to feel about starting secondary school tomorrow?

2   Why do you think that the play begins and ends at the Creek?

3   Draw a picture of Monnie as she is when she finally appears to Hazel and Frankie.

4   Imagine that you are Monnie. Write out what you tell to your new friends in the sea about your old friends on the land and what happened to you when you lived there.

2 Explorations

Monsters

a) Make your own horror story ...

Find a partner and each tell the other a ghost or horror story other than 'Frankenstein'

Together, write down all the things about the stories which you found frightening or horrific. Also, think about how the stories began and ended. Were there any surprises or could you tell what was going to happen next?

Decide on a title for your own, new horror story. Write a short description of where it will be set. Make a list of the characters saying a little bit about each one.

Now, write a first (rough) draft of your story together. Tell it to the rest of your class and, from their reactions to it, work out what to re-write to make the final (best) draft even better. Discuss with your class why people like to tell and be frightened by horror stories.

b) Make your own monster ...

Write down on a large sheet of paper all the different feelings, thoughts and phrases which are raised for you when you hear the word 'monster'

Take another large sheet of paper and draw separate pictures of all the things described in words on the first sheet.

Cut out the pictures and stick them together on to a third sheet of paper to 'put together' (a bit like Frankenstein did) the pieces to create your very own monster.

Write a caption to go with your picture describing the eating and living habits of your monster.

c) Bringing Monnie to life

Get into groups of five and, using each other, movement and sound, find a way of bringing the descriptions of Monnie below to life. Try to show how she grows and changes so much from the first time we see her to the last.

1) *'I looked at the test tube. It was about a quarter full of some greyish, lumpy stuff like badly cooked porridge, only more transparent. It did not move'.*
    The novel, Chapter One

2) *'Quivering, quivering*   *Pop goes the skin*
    Shivering grey,   *Out comes a tentacle*
    Lump of goo   *Feeling the floor*
    With see-through skin   *Spreading its slithering*
    And bright red slits   *Squirming jelly in search*
    Were eyes might be.   *Of food.'*
    The play, Act One: Scene Three

3) *'It began twisting its slit of a mouth in a most ridiculous manner. Now it would bend the corners down until it looked like a croquet hoop; now up into a capital U. Once it even managed to twist it into a figure eight. I couldn't help laughing at it. It didn't seem to know what a mouth was for. It never opened it, not once. Perhaps it wasn't a proper mouth at all.'*
    The novel, Chapter Four

4) *'Monnie had changed. The jelly-like substance that had given it the semi-transparent look had worn off in patches, or perhaps been*

absorbed into the body. This gave it an odd, mottled appearance like a peeling wall. On either side of its head, where its ears should have been, it had grown a vertical fringe of delicate tendrils, like thin green ribbons, covering small slits that opened and shut continually. Its feet were large and floppy and toeless. It had only ten fingers now, but they were all on its right hand. Its crimson eyes were bright.'
The novel, Chapter Nine

5) *'And there, standing there, tall and high,*
Stretching, glittering, towering,
Hands like metal reaching up to the sky;
Its head crowned by a fin yellow as a cockatoo's crest;
Its shoulders wide as a boat;
Green tendrils fluttering like seaweed
From its silvery wet cheeks.
The play, Act Two: Scene Nine

Discuss with your class the ways in which Monnie differs from the more usual images people tend to have of monsters.

d) Monsters are never what you expect

Get into groups of five or six and discuss how much you go on outside appearances when you react to other people or creatures.

Next, act out a scene in which *either* someone who looks like a monster is proved to be all the things that monsters are not meant to be *or* someone who looks like an angel is proved to be a real 'monster' inside.

Share your scene with other groups and discuss how we can get past appearances when we approach others.

Prejudice

a) 'Someone so young and so female ...' (Act One: Scene Two)

Frankie is given very little opportunity in her family to show what she can do or to have her opinions heard. Why does the fact that she is a girl and the youngest make life so tough for her?

Mark three columns on a sheet of paper. Title the first column 'Females', the second column 'Males' and the third column 'Both'.

Which of the jobs below are usually done by females, which by males and which are done by men and women equally? Write the job under the right heading. For example, if you think that roughly the same number of men and women are taxi drivers, put 'taxi drivers' in the 'Both' column:

taxi driver	nurse	doctor	teacher	scientist
child-minder	engineer	dancer	writer	singer
builder	cleaner	chef	pilot	thief
secretary	explorer	artist	plumber	shop keeper

Compare lists with other members of your class and see if you think the same or differently. Why do you think that so many jobs are done particularly by men or women? Why are there some jobs which both men and women do equally?

In groups, act out what happens when *either* a woman tries to do a job usually done by a man *or* a man tries to do a job usually done by a woman.

What can be done to allow people to do jobs they feel best-suited for regardless of whether they are male or female?

b) Attitudes to aliens

In threes, take a cardboard box, seal it with sticky-tape and place it on the floor.

Improvise a scene in which three characters have found this box and know that there is an alien from outer space in it. Character A is afraid; character B is interested; and character C is foolish. They have been told to deal with the box in the interests of humanity. What happens ...?

Discuss with the rest of the class what happened in your scene. How did the group decide what to do? Was it a good decision?

Write a story about what happens when an 'alien' person or people arrive on a small island one day.

c) Closed minds

Prejudice means having formed a strong idea that something or someone is bad without really knowing very much about them.

List all the effects people or groups of peoples being prejudiced can have on individuals in particular and society as a whole.

Using these words or phases as a starting point, write a poem about a time when prejudice (either your own or someone else's towards you) has affected your life.

Science and Society

a) The wonders of science

In Act One: Scene One, Frankie and Hazel say that science can do things which people used to imagine could only be done by magic.

What do you think is the difference between magic and science?

Here are some scientific discoveries or inventions. What differences (if any) have they made to the world in which we live?

telephone	vaccinations	nuclear power
aeroplane	plastic	anaesthetics
wheel	gunpowder	

Either imagine a world in which there was no scientific study or invention. Draw a picture or write a short description of how you think it would look. *Or* imagine a world where science has solved all the world's problems. Draw a picture or write a short description of how life would be then.

b) Animal experiments

In the play, David says that you have to be prepared 'to cut things up' in order to understand how life works. Why does he believe this? What do you think about this attitude?

In small groups, discuss which of the following 'causes' justifies experimenting with or on live animals in ways which will cause them discomfort and pain:

i)   discovering a cure for cancer
ii) testing the effects of a cure for the common cold
iii) testing the effects of a new eye-shadow on the skin
iv) putting animals in the freezing cold in order to find ways of protecting humans working in the Antarctic
v)   sending animals into space to see how it affects living creatures before sending astronauts
vi) testing the efficiency of a new rat poison

After the discussion, try to come up with a statement which sums up your group's conclusions about when it is right (if ever) and when it is wrong to experiment on animals.

There is an article in the local newspaper about an Animal Rights Activist who says that 'those who experiment on animals must be stopped at any cost. We are prepared to send letter bombs to the homes of these torturers if that is what it takes to stop them doing their evil work.' Write a letter to the editor, agreeing or disagreeing with this attitude and planned course of action.

Bringing the play to life

a) Making pictures

In groups of six or seven, brainstorm and write down on a large sheet of paper all the moments in the play which have stuck in your minds as important in some way.

Put these moments in chronological order, i.e. the one that happens first at the beginning to the one that happens last at the end.

Acting out the characters, create a frozen picture of each moment. Link all the frozen pictures together to tell your 'highlight' version of *The Monster Garden*.

Share your picture story with the other groups in the class and discuss what similarities and differences there are between them.

b) Looking at characters

Choose a human character from *The Monster Garden* who you'd like to play – it would be good if every character was played by at least one person in your class.

Act out being your character in each of the following situations:

i)   getting up in the morning
ii) going shopping
iii) having an accident
iv) dealing with being locked out of where you live
v) doing your favourite hobby
vi) finding a dead bird on your doorstep
vii) going for a swim

Find a partner and discuss what sort of relationship your two characters have in the play. Act out the scene you like most between these characters (if they aren't in any scenes together, work out what would happen if they were). Create a frozen picture of the most important moment for the characters' relationship in that scene.

Write a few lines about how your character feels at the beginning and the end of the play about every other character (including Monnie) in *The Monster Garden*.

c) Design

Agree with the rest of your class what shape the stage will be and where the audience will be sitting. For example will it be round or square? Will the audience be on one side or all around?

In groups, draw an outline of the stage shape and list all the different settings that will be needed, e.g. the Creek, Frankie's bedroom.

Approach A: Try to create the settings as realistically as you can. Work out what objects, props, scenery, furniture, back cloths you will need for each scene and draw a plan showing where they would go on the stage.

Approach B: Try to create the feeling or impression of each setting rather than the reality of it. Think of as *few* objects as possible that could be used to represent the key items in each scene, e.g. what could be used to stand for a rock in the Creek, the Steins' breakfast table and Frankie's bed. Draw a plan of each scene showing how your few objects could be placed to create a different effect for each setting.

Choose which of the above design styles you like best – you can always combine bits from each – and share your scene plans with the rest of the class.

d) Narrating

In groups of four or five, look at the Act One: Scene Three in which the thunderstorm brings Monnie to life. Read through each of the narrator's speeches, sitting in a circle and taking turns to read out one line each. Experiment with different ways of sharing out the lines – two people reading two lines together, two lines each etc. Finally, choose the way that gets across the meaning of the lines best and sounds most dramatic.

Stand up and walk round the room saying the lines. Again, try lots of different positions and groupings. Finally, decide on the best positionings and present your work to the rest of the class.

Does a particular type of character develop for you as you say your lines? Who are you? Why are you telling this story? What effect do you want to have on the audience?

e) Making Monnie

In groups of four or five, act out the end of Act Two: Scene Seven in which Monnie saves Frankie from drowning in one of the following ways:

i)   using torchlight to create the effect of Monnie
ii) using a sheet to create the effect of Monnie
iii) using just group body movement to create the effect of Monnie
iv) using rope to create the effect of Monnie
v)   using any combination of the above
vi) using your own objects or costume design

OTHER TITLES IN THIS SERIES

Children's Ward   Age 12+

Paul Abbott, John Chambers and Kay Mellor
Granada TV

Six scripts from the popular Granada TV series Children's Ward. The plays trace the fortunes of patients admitted to the children's ward and the relationships between them.

Children's Ward also examines the way the programmes are made, and is an excellent medium for discussing the nature of television drama.

ISBN: 435 23285 1

Whale

Age 10+

David Holman

Whale is based on the real events of October 1988 when three Californian grey whales became trapped under the Arctic ice-cap in Alaska. The play captures the suspense of the rescue and sees the incident through the eyes of both adults and the children who supported the campaign.

Whale offers many discussion possibilities on green issues, the role of the media and Inuit culture and way of life. The introduction and notes supply ideas, background information and activities for using these opportunities to the full.

ISBN: 435 23286 X